Also by Willy Ley

Adventures of a Romantic Naturalist:

THE LUNGFISH, THE DODO, AND THE UNICORN

DRAGONS IN AMBER

Other Books:

ENGINEERS' DREAMS

ROCKETS, MISSILES, AND SPACE TRAVEL

THE CONQUEST OF SPACE (*with Chesley Bonestell*)

Salamanders and Other Wonders

Still More Adventures of a Romantic Naturalist

by *WILLY LEY*

With Illustrations by OLGA LEY

1955

New York • *The Viking Press*

"The Abominable Snowman" appeared in *Maclean's,*
"The Little People" in *Other Worlds.*

Library of Congress catalog card number: 55-7630

Contents

Illustrations

The animal shown on the title page is the blind Texas cave
    salamander *Typhlomolge rathbuni*

Foreword

When, during the hot summer days of 1948 in Washington, D. C., I went over the page proofs of *The Lungfish, the Dodo, and the Unicorn*, I sometimes found myself under the impression that this was the first of three books. Not, mind you, that the book might be followed by another one, which is almost the customary fate of any factual book, but that it would be the first of three. I don't know whether I mentioned this to anyone then, but if I had I would have been unable to answer the question of what the other two would contain. Well, the "Second *Lungfish*," as it was casually called while it was in the process of writing, appeared in 1950 under the title *Dragons in Amber*.

This, now, is the book which in my mind is the "Third *Lungfish*," although I realize that this is purely a personal opinion. Each of the three books is, and should be, an independent unit, and if a critic should tell me that *Salamanders* is very different from, say, *Dragons in Amber*, I'll simply accept his statement.

As I write this, I am looking at one of the tall bookshelves in my study, and, being busy with a foreword, I find myself wondering whether the foreword in any of the several hundred books I see was actually written first, before the author turned to Chapter I, paragraph 1. I doubt it very much, for the normal procedure is to write the foreword last. It is the author's equivalent of the architect's last look around, when he mentally reviews the original plan and thinks of the changes that occurred while the work was going on.

Discounting the fact that a few chapters turned out somewhat shorter and most of the others considerably longer than I had originally expected, there were relatively few changes from the original concept. I had set out to assemble the case histories of several species that came close to extinction in our time—some even being reported extinct—but managed to survive, sometimes with the aid of man. That became Part III of the book. I had set out to find, if possible, the truth behind a few wild stories which are vaguely known to every naturalist (and are most decidedly known to be ridiculous). By sheer accident these wild stories all concerned trees, so they were logically grouped together in Part II. I also intended to assemble the stories behind some facts about which there was a noticeable amount of controversy, stories involving principles—and, in one case, political issues which actually converted a small, inoffensive, and in all probability not very bright salamander into an item of international dispute.

But although I approached the various chapters in the spirit of "let's find out what can be found," I realize that all of them can be construed as examples of the pattern which Toynbee has labeled "challenge and response." The challenge in most cases was more or less the same; the response never was. Living Nature has too many resources to become monotonous or even objectionably repetitious.

Life, some scientists have said, is a fundamentally improbable chemical reaction. If that is true, it is only logical that something which represents an improbable reaction to begin with will go merrily on to produce more of the same.

WILLY LEY

New York City
May 1955.

Part One

PROBLEMS
OF THE PAST

Nature, the living current of her powers
Was never bound to Day and Night and Hours;
She makes each form by rules that never fail
And 't is not Force, even on a mighty scale.

—Goethe, *Faust,* ii (7860-7864)

1: Cave Salamanders
and High Politics

LET me begin by stating the name of the little animal in question. It is olm, pronounced with a clearly audible "l" in the middle so that there can be no confusion with Mr. Ohm of electrical fame. I know that the name was introduced into scientific literature by the philosopher Lorenz Oken, but I don't know its meaning, if any. The animal's scientific name is *Proteus anguinus.*

With these two statements we have exhausted the simple portion of the story. Everything else is complicated.

Even the location of the olm's rather restricted habitat is not easy to explain. It is a mountainous area in southern Europe, at the northern end of the Balkan peninsula, which was long known as the Krain. The name, of Slavonic origin, happens to mean "edge," representing the view of people who lived on the northern slopes of the Alps. But you won't find that name on modern maps any more, so let's just say that if you move inland from the Trieste area you are in the general neighborhood. The habitat of the olm covers portions of Herzegovina, Istria, and Dalmatia—recently its picture entered the realm of philately on a Yugoslavian postage stamp—and seems to be centered on a place called Adelsberg. There are numerous large caves in the mountains there, most of them encapsuling subterranean lakes which are cold the

3

year round and in eternal darkness except for the occasional
torches of tourist guides.

The people who live near the rivers which empty into the
northern portion of the Aegean Sea have known for many
centuries that a strange inhabitant might appear in their
rivers on occasion. This happened only in spring, when the
snows were melting in the mountains, and, as was realized
later, the hidden lakes of subterranean caves were flooded to
overflowing. This rare visitor was known by the strange name
of "human fish"—presumably because of its very pale and
only slightly pinkish color, since there was nothing else even
remotely "human" about it. At first glance the olm looks like
a small, whitish eel, about a foot long when full grown. For
that length I am deferring to the authority of the *Cambridge
Natural History, Brehm's Tierleben,* and similar learned
works; personally I have never seen an olm that looked more
than 8 inches long.

If you look more closely you see that the apparent eel has
a few appendages which a real eel does not have. Right
behind the head there are two pinkish bundles of external
gills, very much like those of the Mexican axolotl, though
much smaller. And then you notice, set far apart on the
slender and flexible body, four tiny legs, like those of a newt,
but ridiculously out of proportion in their smallness. There
are no eyes, although one can see clearly where the eyes ought
to be. The olm is blind, having no use for eyes in the cold
dark caves where it normally lives. The folklore of the areas
where the olm put in sporadic appearances succeeded in
making the small and completely helpless victim of overflowing lakes into a "dragon"; apparently it was thought, or
at least asserted, that these creatures were the young of terrible monsters which inhabited the interior. If anybody had
tried in early times to arrive at the truth from the welter of
conflicting stories, he would probably have failed.

Though the area where the olm may be found is comparatively small, the animal is not actually rare in its habitat,

and it is therefore surprising that it entered into literature as late as it did. The first name of a person linked with the olm is that of its "discoverer," the man who first wrote about it in sober descriptive terms in 1741. He was "Krain's chronicler," the Baron von Valvasor. A few decades later, a specimen, after changing hands several times, reached the study of the zoologist Laurenti in Vienna. He affixed the name *Proteus anguinus* to it. Proteus, in mythology, was Neptune's herdsman, who could change his shape at will; the second part of the name comes from the Latin *anguis,* meaning

The Balkan cave salamander olm *(Proteus anguinus),* natural colorless form, average length 10 inches

snake. Laurenti had no difficulty in establishing the true nature of the "new" animal. It was evidently a "tailed amphibian," related to the newts and salamanders. Its lack of color and its blindness were simply the result of living in dark caves.

The word "amphibian," derived from Greek *amphis,* meaning "double" or "both," and Greek *bios,* meaning "life," had been coined to indicate that animals of this type were equally at home on land and in water—fresh water, that is. Frogs and toads—the "tail-less amphibians"—are both the best-known and the simplest examples. After beginning with

a water-bound tadpole stage, they climb onto the land when
they reach adulthood and do well in the open air, although a
great fondness for water remains with them for the rest of
their lives. Although the olm was an amphibian by bodily
organization, the term obviously did not apply to its habits.
As far as one could tell it stayed in water all its life, and
though it grew lungs—very simple, so to speak "unfinished"
lungs—it never shed its gills and had forgone the inherent possibility of climbing on land. This looked like one more adaptation to its environment; presumably it found enough food
to live on in the waters of its caves but could find no food
above the water level.

At this point it is necessary to introduce formally another
tailed amphibian, which has already been mentioned: the
Mexican axolotl. It should have been known to zoologists at
the time the Baron von Valvasor wrote about the olm for the
first time, for the axolotl had been described by Francesco
Hernandez as early as 1628 as "a kind of Mexican fish with
soft skin and four feet like those of lizards."[1] But the axolotl
had been forgotten until Alexander von Humboldt brought
two specimens from Mexico to Europe. They were carefully
described by Georges de Cuvier, and *Ambystoma tigrinum*
became the scientific name. Here was another tailed amphibian that lived in water all its life, never shed its gills,
and never crawled up on the land. Cuvier himself did not
find it easy to believe this; the specimens brought by von
Humboldt looked too much like newt larvae, the equivalent
of the tadpole stage of the tail-less amphibia. However, all
the statements from the New World agreed that the axolotl
only grew larger with age and did not change. Cuvier died in
1832 and never learned anything about the strange Mexican

---

[1] Hernandez had been the body physician of Philip II of Habsburg, king of
Spain, and had been sent to Mexico by his royal master to collect "natural
curiosities." His book, printed in Rome in 1628, had the longish title: *Rerum
medicarum novae Hispaniae thesaurus seu plantarum, animalium, mineralium
Mexicanorum historia. . . .* Francesco Hernandez was also the first to describe
the Gila monster *(Heloderma)* and the so-called "horned toad" *(Phrynosoma).*

amphibian that would have made him realize that his first suspicions had been correct.

Other zoologists were not sure what to think. More reports from Mexico said that the axolotl was common, that it was brought to market for food by the thousands, always with a conspicuous growth of external gills. (Old Hernandez had

The axolotl of Mexico, actually the permanent larval form of the tiger salamander

also known that it resembled eel in taste.) The American zoologist Spencer Fullerton Baird, later secretary of the Smithsonian Institution and first United States Fish Commissioner, was virtually the only expert who stated his doubts clearly. In his opinion, he said, the tadpole-like characteristics of the axolotl were far too pronounced for it to be considered as anything but the larval stage of a salamander. He added that the fact that adult specimens were not known did not prove that they didn't exist.

Sometime during 1864 the *Jardin d'acclimation* in Paris received six axolotl, five males and one female. They were placed into a suitable aquarium and for about a year they lived an uneventful life. On February 18, 1865—Monsieur A. Duméril, in charge of this section of the institute, carefully noted the dates—they suddenly became active. The males pursued the female and discharged their semen into the water and the following day the solitary female began to lay eggs. Monsieur Duméril had his assistants cut the plants to which the eggs were attached and put them into another and empty aquarium. Being an experienced man he knew that the term "cannibalism" is no insult to amphibians, and that the eggs, likely as not, might be eaten. And he did not want to lose them; axolotls in captivity were very rare. Six weeks later the whole story was repeated and another bunch of cut water plants was transferred to still another aquarium.

Most of the eggs proved to have been fertilized and about a month after they had been laid the tiny larvae began to appear. First they grew their gills, still out of their body resources; then the membranes that closed their mouths burst suddenly and they began to hunt without unnecessary delay. By the beginning of September (1865) they had almost reached the size of their parents. And by the end of September one of them began to change. The gills reduced in size, the finny fringe around the tail began to shrink, the shape of the head changed, and numerous small yellowish-white spots began to dot the hitherto uniformly dark skin. On September 28 a second began the transformation, on October 7 a third, and on October 10 a fourth. They became adult salamanders. Cuvier's early doubts and Baird's steadfast belief had been fully vindicated.

The first thing Duméril tried to do was to see whether the change could be brought about artificially. He removed the gills of a number of axolotl, but on one side only, so that they would not suffocate. The animals promptly grew new ones. Duméril reported later that some of the specimens had lost and regrown their gills on both sides (removed alternately) as many as six times and had not shown any signs of suffering. A few of those on which Duméril had operated did acquire the adult form later, but Duméril himself said that they might have done so without his surgical interference. And the majority of the axolotl simply stayed in the water.

The disturbing thing was not that a few axolotl had assumed the adult form. That such an adult form existed had been suspected by many, and believed by a few, all along. What was disturbing was that, under conditions excluding any chance of observational error, the larvae had mated and propagated. This had always been considered not only the privilege but the purpose of the adults. It was as if somebody had reported mating and egg-laying caterpillars. If caterpillars could do that, there would be no reason for the butterfly. If tadpoles could propagate the race, the adult frog became superfluous. But the axolotl, while in an undisputed larval stage, had done just that.

Before any conclusions could be drawn, more information was needed. The idea of how this could be obtained came from Professor August Weismann, who had originally studied medicine but had soon switched over to biology. Weismann said that natural conditions in Mexico apparently favored a continued larval stage and were unfavorable to the adult stage. Salamanders need moisture all their lives. They prefer moist forests, swampy meadows with underbrush; in short, they live up to the term amphibian and like surroundings which a mammal would find too wet and a fish consider too dry. If no moist forest can be had they'll take to wet caves. Presumably moist forests and wet caves were not too frequent in Mexico. But in artificial surroundings one could create conditions which were inconvenient to the larval axolotl and favored the adult salamander.

A then well-known German lady naturalist, who happened to live in Freiburg in the Breisgau, the city where the "powder monk" Berthold the Black is supposed to have invented gunpowder and guns, attacked this wholly unmilitary problem. Her name was Marie von Chauvin. She had five specimens of axolotl to work with, the survivors of a shipment of one dozen; they were about a week old when they reached her. By dint of careful temperature control of the water and equally careful feeding Marie von Chauvin succeeded in keeping them alive and once they started growing everything went well. After about five months she noticed that one always stayed near the surface of the water. She took this one and placed it in another container with a carefully contrived landscape. Much of this was land, with moss growing thickly on the highest point. The watery area was such that the axolotl, if it stayed in the water, was usually partly exposed to air; there was only one place where it could submerge completely.

The physical changes first observed by Duméril took just four days. On the fifth day the animal shed its skin and the adult form was complete. Three weeks later three more axolotl seemed ready. They were transferred and changed too, one of them as quickly as the first, the two others needing a little over a week. The fifth specimen, which had always been the weakest and smallest, took much longer; a full two weeks after transfer it was barely able to leave the water. If it was exposed to the air for too long, its skin began to discolor, it exuded a typical smell which Fräulein von Chauvin knew from other salamanders and called the "fear smell," and it was obviously suffering. Brought back to the deepwater aquarium it submerged to the bottom at once and recovered, the gills, which had already been shrinking, returning to full size. Repeated attempts to make it change always ended in the same manner.

Fräulein von Chauvin's work demonstrated that the axolotl, like its many relatives in the United States, does change into the adult form when encouraged by its environment. (Specimens have been found in the open since then.) But it does not have to change. If it is necessary, or just more convenient, to stay in the water, the larvae, without losing any of their larval characteristics, mature sexually and breed. This unsuspected phenomenon required a special term; I don't know who thought it up but whoever did it displayed a touch of professorial humor. He coined the term "neoteny" for larval propagation, from Greek *neos,* meaning "new," "recent," or "young," and Greek *teinō* which means "to stretch." There was some disagreement among the theorists whether neoteny should be considered "progressive" or not. Some inclined to the view that any successful adaptation to environment (and presumed environmental changes) should be called progress, since the alternative was extinction. Since survival was obviously superior to extinction, this flexible or "stretchable" sex arrangement was a kind of progress. Others, notably August Weismann, considered that full metamorphosis was the goal, that it had once been the norm among the axolotl, presumably until a climatic change took place in Mexico, and that neoteny therefore was "retrograde evolution." So far this was just talk inside the scientific fraternity, of which nobody outside the immediate field knew anything.

During the second half of the nineteenth century the tribe of the fish fanciers had begun to flourish in Europe, especially strongly, it seems, in Austria, Germany, and neighboring Russia. These fish fanciers did not have professional training, but their enthusiasm rivaled that of the professionals, and since many of them had what the busy professors lacked, namely time, they contributed quite a number of new observations. The professionals looked upon their efforts with some friendliness but maintained a proper distance (most especially from those whose hobby assumed commercial aspects), which they expressed by referring to the amateurs as *Aquarianer.*

The fraternity of the *Aquarianer* had meanwhile discovered the olm, to such an extent that a few people in Trieste and vicinity had the words "Olm Dealer" printed on their business cards. The olm was easy to keep; it did not require much more than cold water—around 50 degrees Fahrenheit—and live food, consisting of tiny crustaceans and small worms. It wasn't much of an exhibit, though, for the aquarium had to be kept in darkness; when one approached with a light the olms became irritated and hid away behind stones or in cracks. But though the olm did not adapt itself to light, it was soon learned that the temperature of the water did not matter too much. Olms could be kept in water of room temperature and no harm seemed to be done. Surprisingly, the olm turned out to be extremely sensitive to vibration—apparently a vibration in its subterranean lakes is a danger signal.

The reports on the axolotl naturally raised quite a number of questions about the olm. That it was blind and colorless could be ascribed to the permanent darkness of the cave lakes, but had this environment also forced it into the status of a permanent larva? Was there an "adult" stage and how did it look? Was the olm's love life another example of neoteny? And was there any way to find out? The information was meager, to say the least. In an aquarium olms inevitably stayed close to the bottom, except when food was thrown in. On occasion, if the water was "not fresh" (or possibly too warm) they were seen to rise to the surface to breathe air. The tourist guides claimed that they had sometimes seen olms out of the water, but very close to the water's edge. People who had kept half a dozen olms in the same aquarium stated that they saw them play on occasion but that they had never observed a mating. And nobody had ever seen either the eggs of an olm or a very small specimen.

A number of researchers went to work, following the procedure which had been so successful in Fräulein von Chauvin's observations of the axolotl. Needless to say, she herself was one of the researchers. It was established that an olm when unable to immerse in water died within two to four hours, no matter how moist the air. When they were kept in very shallow water their lungs would grow, but not to the point of making the gills superfluous. And removing the gills simply killed them, although the more robust axolotls had grown new ones. In 1875 there came some positive news from one of the tourist guides, a man named Prelessnig. He kept two specimens and one morning he found fifty-eight eggs in the container. Since the two sexes look alike to human eyes Prelessnig could not tell whether his specimens were both female or whether one was a male, and if both were female whether one or both had laid the eggs. The eggs did not hatch.

Seven years later Fräulein von Chauvin actually observed a female olm attach its eggs to a rock. She provided a description of the eggs and also a description of the way the olms changed at mating time so that a good observer could tell the males and females apart temporarily. But there her story stopped. Another six years later, in 1888, the olms kept by E. Zeller laid seventy-six eggs. This happened during the two nights between April 14 and 16. Zeller waited for the eggs to hatch. The wait was complicated by one thing and aggravated by another. The complication was that nobody knew how much time normally went by between the laying and the hatching of the eggs. The aggravating factor was that eggs laid by other olms in captivity had not hatched, although at least Marie von Chauvin had been sure that they had been fertilized. It was a long wait—and the wonder is that Zeller did not throw out the eggs in the meantime—but 90 days later two larvae appeared. They were just a little less than one inch in length and resembled the adult specimens quite closely, but had much better defined, though of course much smaller, eyes.

Just at that time somebody called Zeller's attention to an article in an old scientific journal, the *Isis* (published, incidentally, by Lorenz Oken) for the year 1831. The article was signed Michahelles, but he was merely the reporter. The body of the piece, which was later dubbed the Protocol of Stratil, had been formally written down by the landowner J. Geck von Verch, who was also the county judge; hence his highly "official" style. He "deposed and said" that on June 17, 1825, he, "in common with several members of my family and members of my neighbors' families," had seen an olm give birth to a live young. The length was 1½ inches; it looked, except for size, just like the mother, except that it had two black dots "like poppyseeds" where one should expect to find the eyes, though the eyes of the mother "are grown over with skin and not visible." All this was much too definite to be brushed aside, nor did Zeller try to brush it aside. He merely said that this report was unique. But so was his own; nobody else had ever seen an olm egg hatch either.

The next report, which failed to shed any light on the main problem, came from Lemberg in 1904 and had the amusing aspect that it originated with somebody who was not interested in investigating the olm's life history. He was Professor Nusbaum, who in early fall of 1903 paid a visit to "the olm dealer Wilhar in Grosstock near Adelsberg" and selected five specimens which had been caught a few weeks earlier. He had them sent to Lemberg.

When they arrived, during the early part of September, I put them in a round glass container with clean water from the faucet which was changed once or twice per week. I placed the aquarium on the window sill of the laboratory, where it was well illuminated. Since the animals were meant to be used for anatomical and histo-logical research I made no effort to feed them since they were in good health and I knew from experience that the olm will last for a long time without food. After two months two specimens were killed and dissected; it turned out that one of them was a male. Since the three others did not eat the finely chopped meat offered and since the early winter made it impossible to breed live food for them they stayed without any food in clean tap water for the whole period of their captivity until October 1904.

They did lose some weight but were always alert and brisk in their movements; since they were well illuminated they acquired a dark brownish-blackish pigmentation over the whole body. After a few months had gone by I noticed that one of the three specimens appeared somewhat heavier and more sluggish than the two others.

On October 12, 1904, after they had been in captivity for about 13 months I entered the laboratory as usual at about 8 o'clock in the morning and when I looked at the aquarium with the olms I saw to my utmost surprise that there was a fourth specimen, young, very skinny, and pale (the old ones, as stated, had turned a brownish-black), moving about very feebly. It had indubitably been born alive during the night or during the early morning hours.

The young olm died by noon. Two days later Professor Nusbaum killed the specimen which he thought to have been the mother and found that the left oviduct was still greatly enlarged while the other appeared normal. Nusbaum ascribed the whole incident to his mistreatment of the animals, which he had not intended for breeding.

The organism of the mother was in captivity for over a year without any nourishment, living in clear tap water which could hardly have contained anything for it to eat. . . . The adverse condition, namely the bright light, the lack of rock cavities and normal bottom, the lack of food and possibly the wrong temperature, all this together probably brought it about that the female did not lay the fertilized eggs as they entered the oviduct. Only one egg, presumably the outermost one, hatched and the other eggs served as food for this one larva.

Professor Nusbaum observed correctly and reasoned well. If only his goal had been different the University of Lemberg could have won a victory over a scientific institution in Vienna, the Institute for Experimental Biology of the University of Vienna.

Physically this institute was located in rather unacademic surroundings, namely in the Prater, Vienna's unique amuse-

ment area. Before the university took over the building it
had been a public aquarium and at some time further in the
past the recesses which later held the large exhibition aquaria
are said to have been *chambres séparées* for amorous purposes. But by the year 1900 all activities in this building
were very respectable, although later critics said that they
were not wholly scientific.

The basement of the building contained an old cistern and
if somebody had tried to produce an artificial cave ideal for
the olm he could not have done better than the forgotten
architect who had built the house. The masonry which
formed the ceiling of the basement was below ground level
and water had oozed through it for long enough to produce
actual if tiny stalactites. The basement was windowless, so that
Stygian darkness was the normal and prevailing condition.
And no matter what the season or the weather outside, the
temperature in the cistern stayed between 50 and 55 degrees
Fahrenheit. Normally one could not enter the basement at
any time without getting one's feet wet above the ankles;
when the university took over the building it was considered
part of general maintenance to pump the water out. But one-
quarter of the area, measuring about 120 square feet, was
enclosed by a foot-high cement wall and filled to the top with
well water. In December 1903 this subterranean basin was
stocked with forty full-grown olms. The avowed purpose was
to find out, once and for all, how olms propagate, and because
of this purpose the specimens purchased were the largest
which the dealers had to offer. One died soon; the other
thirty-nine ate tubifex worms and tiny fishes voraciously but
were indifferent to sex in spite of the reputation of the
upstairs rooms.

As has been mentioned, a human observer can tell the sex
of an olm only at mating time, and even then one needs a
small amount of good luck to be right every time. Hence the
large number of animals—it was more than unlikely that all
thirty-nine of them would be of the same sex; the very idea

was preposterous. The young biologist in charge of the experiment was a Dr. Paul Kammerer. For quite a long time he checked every day, eagerly and attentively. He knew that Marie von Chauvin and Zeller and a few others had seen olms lay eggs. On the other side there was the very formal "protocol" of the old county judge, which was then unique[2] as an observation but had the backing of many of the guides, who "knew" that the olm gave birth to live young even though they had not seen it happen themselves. The amphibian method of giving birth to live offspring, it may be remarked, is simply not to lay the eggs, thus allowing them to hatch inside the mother's body. The technical term is "ovoviviparous," as distinct from "oviparous" (laying eggs) and "viviparous" (having babies). It was certainly possible, as one or two biologists had said, that "since we don't really know anything about the olm the possibility must be admitted that there are two species, as hard to tell from each other as are the sexes, but distinguished sharply by the fact that one is oviparous and the other ovoviviparous."

No matter who might prove to be correct in the end, the thirty-nine olms in the basement were interested only in food. After a year Kammerer grew somewhat tired, after another half-year very much so, and, as he confessed, "my control became lax and the feeding irregular." In October 1905, during one of his by then rather rare trips to the basement, he noticed that the basin contained a few olms which were several inches shorter than the average. But he did not feel sure that they were young ones. He had been rather remiss in feeding the olms and he knew very well that certain invertebrate animals will shrink in size when fasting. These might be unfortunate individuals who had been slower than the others on the occasions when food had been brought. Upstairs in the same building a graduate student (Weindl was his name), experimenting with other olms, had starved some, to see whether pigmentation was influenced by nutri-

2 This was just before Nusbaum made his observations.

tion, and found that the treatment had reduced their size though it had not influenced the pigmentation.

But in May 1906 there were again several very small animals in the basin and their eyes proved that they were young ones. On October 4, 1907, Kammerer spied an olm which looked like a pregnant female. He fished out the unusually large specimen and put it in a separate jar, which, however, he left in the basement so as not to change any of the other factors of the environment. In the evening of October 18 Kammerer believed that the animal was dying because of its helpless attitude in the water—typical of a disease of salamanders—but in the morning of October 19 the animal was normal, and in the company of two young ones, each nearly 4 inches long.

His interest in the olm restored, Kammerer proceeded to prove that the idea of two species of olm, characterized by different methods of reproduction although otherwise undistinguishable, had been what Kammerer's North German colleagues call a *Schnapsidee,* meaning nonsense. Ovoviviparous propagation is the rule and what Nusbaum had ascribed to unusual conditions was "normal" for an olm. One egg hatches in the oviduct (either in one oviduct only or one in each) and the additional eggs which are produced dissolve to a liquid which feeds the one that is developing. But if the water is too warm—over 55 degrees Fahrenheit—this mechanism fails to function properly; presumably the first egg does not hatch, and then all the eggs, up to sixty in number, are laid as eggs. If any of them hatch the young are too small to survive.

Kammerer felt that there were more discoveries to be made. Nusbaum had observed that his carelessly kept olms turned dark. This was not a new discovery, merely a corroboration of a fact noted in many textbooks. The student Weindl had especially studied this pigmentation. Kammerer could easily see that it extended over every square millimeter of the exposed skin, including the skin which grew over the useless eyes. The young olms that had been born in the cold basement had more fully developed eyes than the old ones; this was one of the things Weismann would call retrograde. At one time in the past the olm's ancestors had evidently lived in the open waters and had had functioning eyes. By that time it was established that the olm was not unique and that it had quite a number of rather close relatives in North America. They are the members of the genus *Necturus* which are usually called "mud puppies." They resemble the olm in being permanent larvae, and have lungs and three pairs of bushy red gills that are never shed. But they have functioning eyes, marked coloration, four good legs, and even go on land temporarily—in short, they demonstrate beautifully what the olm probably was like before natural events shut it off in subterranean caves.[3] As Marie von Chauvin, among others, had shown, the olm had "retrogressed" too much to be led, wheedled, or browbeaten into changing into the "adult form" it had once had. But maybe one could at least restore its eyesight.

Simply exposing the young with their better developed

[3] But America has also shown that amphibians belonging to other families can become olmlike in shape. From Virginia down to Florida and in the southern parts of Alabama, Mississippi, and Louisiana you find the genus *Amphiuma* (two subspecies, one with two and one with three toes per foot), popularly known as Congo eels, though they are not eels and are not found in the Congo. Quite hefty—up to 40 inches long—and deep dark brown in color, they resemble the olm *in appearance* because of body shape and the diminutive limbs. But these are merely adaptations to an extreme aquatic life. The tiny (3¾-inch) Ozark blind salamander *(Typhlotriton spelaeus)* is, as its name says, blind, "ghostly pale in color" as one observer expressed it, but still has well-developed legs and may revert to pigmentation. But there are two others which are analogous to the olm and look like it, again except for the longer legs—namely, *Haideotriton* and *Typhlomolge*. The first is known in only one specimen, a 3-inch-long, sexually mature female which was found in a 200-foot well near Albany, Georgia. It was blind and the description read: "In life body pale, pinkish white, vaguely opalescent, viscera and eggs plainly evident through body wall, limbs transparent, the larger blood vessels readily discernible." The other, *Typhlomolge rathbuni*, first became known when an artesian well was drilled in Hays County, Texas, but has also been found in Kendall, Comal, and Crockett counties, all in Texas. It grows to 5½ inches and could easily be called the "Texas olm." But it is only "like" and not related to the Balkan species.

eyes to daylight did not work. The outer skin covered the eyes too, and as the outer skin responded to light by darkening, the eyes were even more effectively shut off. The fact that the animal darkens when exposed to light tends rather quickly to cause one to use the word "exposed" in the sense in which it is used by photographers. It may have been this association of ideas which led Kammerer to try the photographer's red darkroom lamp. The first result obtained was that an olm "exposed" in this manner behaved just like a photographic plate so exposed. There was no reaction, no darkening. Kammerer then tried a kind of alternate exposure. An olm was occasionally exposed to light and to red light between exposures. The specimen used had just been born and for the first year of its life nothing happened. But that literally "nothing" happened, except normal growth, was encouraging. Normally the eyes of the newly born olm are reduced during the first year; the eyes of this specimen stayed as they were. During the second year it enlarged noticeably. During the third year the skin above the eyes began to bulge. During the fourth year corneas seemed to form. And when the specimen was five years old it had clearly visible eyes (see illustration, p. 21), and, of course, a dark skin, although not quite as dark as that of those which had simply been put into an illuminated aquarium at some stage.

One would expect that Kammerer would have repeated the experiment with a number of specimens in the hope of developing eyes in males and females and then seeing whether they would "breed true," producing a form capable of living in open lakes and rivers. But he did not. Instead, he made himself the center of a scientific controversy which, in time, grew into a political issue.

To understand this surprising "development," we have to go back to about the time of the "discovery" of the olm.

On August 1, 1744, the Baron Pierre de Monet, Chevalier de Lamarck, became a father for the eleventh time. The child was a son, who was baptized Jean Baptiste Pierre Antoine. Since the father's income was not at all commensurate with his titles he decided that Jean Baptiste was to be an abbé and had him put into a school for future clergymen. In the process of growing up the young Chevalier de Lamarck must have developed other ideas, for as soon as his father died in 1760 he left the school and joined the army. One year later he participated in a minor battle near the small town of

Five-year-old olm, darkened by exposure to daylight, with re-established and presumably functioning eyes

Lippstadt and attracted attention by his bravery. He was commissioned without a delay and transferred to the garrison of Monaco, where he promptly fell in love—not with a pretty girl but with the interesting and varied vegetation. He immediately began to study botany, without a teacher but very systematically. Pensioned from the army because of sickness, he went to Paris and continued his studies at the botanical garden which was then called the Jardin du Roi. He began a three-volume work on the plants of France, the *Flore française,* and met the famous naturalist Count Buffon at the Jardin du Roi. He attracted favorable attention once more; Buffon saw to it that Lamarck's book was printed and that he was made a "custodian of the herbarium," which was a title with a very small salary attached to it.

With the French revolution the name of the Jardin du Roi was changed to Jardin des Plantes and the Chevalier de Lamarck was henceforth addressed as Citizen Lamarck, but otherwise he was left alone. In short, he was still poor although he was by no means a young man any more. During his fiftieth year he was suddenly offered a professorship. Naturally Citizen Lamarck accepted.

Considering that he could only be labeled a "botanist" because of his earlier work, one would expect that he would have become a professor of botany. But for reasons nobody has ever succeeded in tracing—maybe there weren't any—Lamarck was given the chair of invertebrate zoology. The chair of vertebrate zoology had been given the year before to Geoffroy de Saint-Hilaire, who was a mineralogist. Incidentally, both men did well in their new fields. But Lamarck had either acquired or had always possessed a difficult character. A fairly recent biographer of his has to admit that it is difficult to understand Lamarck or to judge him justly. It was apparently still more difficult for his contemporaries, and Cuvier especially did not have much good to say about him while he was alive. When Lamarck's daughter once said to her aged and blind father, *"La postérité vous admirera"* ("Posterity will admire you"), she may just have been trying to console him, but the words turned out to be curiously prophetic.

The reason for the later admiration was a small volume entitled *Philosophie zoologique,* printed for the first time in 1809. It must have been the result of much thought, but it was apparently written down hastily, for its organization is awkward, the line of reasoning becomes apparent to the reader mostly in retrospect, and the examples given are often poor, sometimes ridiculous, and in all cases insufficient in

number. If one can manage to read this book without allowing oneself to remember things which happened afterward,
one can easily understand why it made little impression on
Lamarck's contemporaries and why Cuvier had no use for it.
The simple historical fact is that nobody paid any attention
to it until after the publication (precisely half a century later)
of Charles Darwin's *Origin of Species*. And even then Lamarck's name was made known mostly by one man, namely
Ernst Haeckel.

The statement of Lamarck's belief which became the main
foundation for his posthumous fame is rather hidden in the
middle of the seventh chapter of the *Philosophie zoologique,*
and consists of two "conclusions" which are contrasted with
each other. The first "conclusion" is labeled as the one
"accepted up to now" and is phrased: "Nature (or its Creator)
when creating the animals foresaw all the possible environments in which they would live and gave to each species a
permanent organization and an unchangeable body which
forces each species to live in the environments and climates
where they are found and to continue in their habits." The
second "conclusion," which Lamarck called simply "my
own," reads: "Nature has produced all the species of animals
in succession. She began with the least perfect or simplest and
finished with the most perfect. She complicated their organization in steps. As the animals spread into all habitable areas
of the globe each species acquired changes in habits and
changes of its organs under the influence of the environment
in which it lived."

This sounds to a modern reader like an early expression
of belief in adaptation and evolution, which is precisely what
it is. The difficulties begin when you start inquiring about
the causes of evolution. Lamarck had used such examples
as wading birds which do not "wish" to wet their bodies but
must live near the water for their food. So they "wish" to
stretch their legs and succeed in doing so, and since the
stretched legs are inherited by their offspring these birds now

look as if they walked on stilts. "You will realize furthermore that the same bird which wants to fish without wetting its body must make steady efforts to elongate its neck."

Lamarck, in short, had drawn the correct conclusion, namely that the species of animals cannot be constant but have to undergo steady change, thereby producing new species. But the mechanism he thought up to account for the changes was decidedly weak, to be gentle about it. And, truth to tell, Charles Darwin did almost the same thing. He convinced everybody interested that the species had changed in the past and that there had to be changes in the future. But again the mechanism he thought up was not convincing, or at least one had the feeling that while it might explain a number of cases, it could not work generally. The scientists who were labeled "followers of Darwin" because they were convinced of the changeability of species, and hence of evolution, were usually *not* followers of Darwin when it came to the mechanism. Their opinions ranged from an uncertain feeling that additional mechanisms should be found—some actually tried to combine Lamarck's and Darwin's ideas on this point—to a firm declaration that the "causes of evolution" (meaning essentially, the mechanism of how evolution occurs) "had still to be found."

The story of the controversy would be a book in itself; in fact, it has been written in the form of a large number of books. But first let us look at a "Darwinian" example to see what the issues were. The North European tree frog *Hyla arborea* has a beautiful green color. When the tree frog is sitting on a leaf this color is obviously of great advantage to the individual and to the continued existence of its species. On the one side, an animal which feeds on frogs may not see the green frog while it would not fail to spot one which was, say, bright yellow. On the other side, the same coloration helps the frog to secure its food simply because its victim may not notice it either. But most frogs have a coloration which is brownish or yellowish with spots or stripes which might be green. Naturally the individuals are not as much alike as so many postage stamps or coins. Some have more green, and they have a somewhat better chance of survival, if only until the time for laying eggs comes around. In the next generation the frogs with more green will be somewhat more numerous and among them there will be some with a still larger proportion of green. Since the ones which have more green on their skins "by chance" (Darwin was careful to say that he used the word chance in its strictest meaning of "from unknown cause") tend to eat better and live longer, an all-green frog will be the final result.

To the best of my knowledge Darwin did not use this example; I made it up with two purposes in mind. It shows the general line of reasoning and it also exhibits a weakness which could be, and would have been, expressed with the counterquestion: "Did a *little* green actually help?" If, among the offspring of multicolored frogs there had been an all-green frog, the rest would sound more convincing by far. But Darwin worked with a little change at a time, every generation, so to speak, progressing by a fraction of an inch. One could find cases where this sounded reasonable, but much was left open to question. As regards our olm, for example, why had it turned colorless even though it has the ability to form pigment? In its dark caves color is completely unimportant; it might just as well have stayed dark.

Science is a self-correcting process, aiming at the best possible explanation, and the more facts that are known the better the explanation is likely to be. What the scientists wanted was facts, more and more facts. And one "fact" which had not been proved to be a fact was crucial with regard to Lamarck's ideas. For Darwin's explanation, the crucial question was whether the small beginnings of a useful chance were useful enough in themselves to last. For Lamarck's, it was whether "acquired characteristics can be inherited."

Professor August Weismann, whose early medical training is quite noticeable in the concept of the experiment, took a number of white mice and amputated their tails. Then he let them mate and amputated the tails of the young mice immediately after birth. He continued this through twenty-two generations, with a total of 1502 mice. Not a single mouse was born without a tail. As soon as he published the result, a naturalist who happened to be Jewish commented that the Jews have practiced circumcision for over three thousand years or about one hundred human generations, but that he had never heard of a Jewish boy baby's being born *sans praeputium*. These two examples seemed to prove all by themselves that acquired characteristics were not inherited.

But the school of thought which believed that such an inheritance had to be possible in order to explain observed facts had an answer ready. "Inner regeneration," they said. To a biologist the word "regeneration," means the regrowth of a part which has been lost. Any newt will regrow a leg which has been bitten off—remember Duméril's experience with the gills of the axolotl. If a bird loses a wing, or a mammal a leg, the limb stays lost, but the young birds hatching from eggs laid after the loss, or the young mammals begotten after the accident, are normal. This is what is meant by "inner regeneration"; in higher animals the individual can no longer be repaired but the species is not impaired by individual misfortune.

The opponents quietly replied that there was no need for such a concept. The examples of the cut-off mouse tails and the accidentally lost limb could be more simply explained by saying that the germ plasm had not been influenced by these circumstances, and that inheritance was determined by the germ plasm. Besides, since the violent loss of a leg did not influence the germ plasm, why should the stretching of a neck do so? In short, the changes have to take place in the germ plasm itself.

How difficult the problem could be is neatly illustrated by what may be called the case of the chilled insects. The European butterfly *Vanessa levana* exists in two versions and this was known to result from temperature influences. If the butterfly emerged from the pupa during the same year, one form resulted; if the butterfly did not emerge until the following spring, the other form occurred. It was an obvious idea to collect pupae in the fall and to keep them in a heated room through the winter, or to take summer pupae and stick them into a refrigerator. It was another obvious idea to freeze pupae more strongly than normal winter would, or to heat them to higher temperatures than normal summer would. The result was that caterpillars collected in Switzerland produced the "regional varieties" of Sweden and of Sardinia in the Mediterranean. When the same experiment was tried with other insects it turned out that chilling the pupa of the potato beetle—an American insect which had already settled in Europe by that time—would darken the finished beetle's wing covers. The offspring of such a darkened beetle had normal color, *unless* the adult beetle was also chilled for some time after it had emerged. And if the pupa was not chilled, but only the finished beetle immediately after emergence, the parent had light wing covers and the next generation was darkened.

According to one party, the fact that it was necessary to chill the adult proved that the cold influenced the germ plasm directly. If you chilled the pupa only you got no result, presumably because the germ plasm was not yet ready at that stage.

Oh no! said the other party. What happens is that the wing covers of the beetle darken and that these darkened wing covers are then transmitted as an inheritance of acquired characteristics. If the just-finished adult beetle is chilled, the mechanism is precisely the same, but the wing covers of the adult are too far finished to show the darkening effect.

Experiments with the olm produced results similar to those obtained with the darkened potato beetle. Kammerer reported that he had taken several olms which had acquired pigmentation because they lived in a lighted aquarium and had put them back into darkness for mating. They were kept in darkness until the young were born. Of course the adults stayed dark-skinned, having once acquired the pigmentation. But the young were born with pigmentation too. This did not convince the other side. Weismann pointed out that the experiment had begun with adult olms which were, of course, transparent. Hence the light had been able to reach the germ plasm and to produce a change there, of course an inheritable change. Kammerer, somewhat miffed, had to admit that the olm's body was transparent. He did not agree with Weismann's interpretation, but he had to accept the fact that two mutually exclusive interpretations were possible.

For the sake of completeness I have to mention that just at about that time Hugo De Vries in Holland observed what he called "mutations"—a phenomenon which, applied to our earlier example, could lead to an all-green frog in one jump. But while his work opened entirely new vistas for both the experimenter and the theorist, it did not stop the fight about the inheritance of acquired characteristics. One side was determined to prove that this was impossible. The other side was equally determined to prove that it was possible and did in fact happen.

Dr. Paul Kammerer made up his mind that he was the man who was going to do the proving. And he was going to work with animals that did not have transparent skins; he was tired of being contradicted. So he started several series of experiments with two animals new to this story: the common black and yellow salamander of Europe (*Salamandra maculosa*) and the midwife toad (*Alytes obstetricans*).

The latter, incidentally also named by Laurenti,[4] is a pretty toad, at the most 2 inches in length, which is rather

---

[4] To avoid misunderstandings I must mention that the *Alytes* in this name is not derived from the Greek word *alytēs* meaning "policeman," but from the Greek *alytos*, which means "firm," in reference to the eggs produced.

common in Portugal, Spain, and France and occurs somewhat more rarely in the western areas of Germany, being
more frequent in the southern portions of these areas. In
color it is a bluish ash-gray on top and a light gray below,
with darker spots. As with many amphibia it is impossible
to tell the sexes apart.

The midwife toad *(Alytes obstetricans)* of Western Europe. Male
with eggs

Except when . . . And that is what made the midwife toad
famous.

Most of the frogs and toads which live on land return to
the water when mating time comes around, for the eggs have
to hatch in water for the sake of the tadpole stage. The midwife toad does not return to the water for mating. This takes
place on land and while it goes on, the male, using his hind
legs, literally pulls the eggs out of the body of the female.

The eggs form a long string, about 30 inches in length, consisting of a jellylike substance in which the eggs are imbedded at regular intervals. While pulling the string of eggs out of the female, the male loops it around his hind legs. When the whole string has been pulled out the male lets go of the female—who has two or three more egg strings forming for additional matings that take place some three weeks apart— and walks off, somewhat clumsily, as can easily be understood.

He then digs himself a hole in moist sand or soil, which he does with great skill and very fast. There he sits with the egg string, waiting quietly while the eggs "ripen." After the waiting period of a few weeks the male appears from his hole and looks for water. This is the time when a human observer can tell the sex of the specimen. Finding water, the male jumps in and starts swimming very energetically. This breaks the egg membranes and the tiny tadpoles scatter in all directions. A few more energetic movements get rid of the empty "hose," and then the toad resumes his normal life, on land. Sometimes a male, disturbed or frightened out of his hole, may sacrifice the egg package for his own safety. It has been observed that the eggs develop just the same even if abandoned, but the tadpoles do not survive being born on land.

It seems reasonable to assume that at some time in the past the midwife toads were far more aquatic in their habits. Though they probably hunted insects and worms on land, they presumably mated in the water just like other toads, and their interesting and unique midwifery somehow started at a later date as an adjustment to an environment that was slowly drying up. These toads had faced the same problem that had confronted the axolotl, or rather its adult form, the tiger salamander. The one had solved it by simply not leaving what water there was left; the other by staying on land completely, with the one exception of that seasonal plunge for the sake of the eggs.

Knowing about the midwife toad's habits, one does not

have to be a partisan of one or the other school of thought about heredity to grow curious. What would happen if the toads were forced to *stay* in water all their lives?

But how could they best be forced? Kammerer reasoned that simply keeping them in an aquarium without any dry land might be too drastic a change, especially since it would also involve a change in feeding habits. For this reason he kept them in a terrarium which offered both land and water. But the temperature was kept around 90 degrees Fahrenheit, a skin-drying temperature for a toad. To escape the heat the toads willingly went into the water and when mating time came they mated in the water. The male did not or could not wind the egg string around its hind legs under the circumstances, and the eggs remained in the water, as is normal with most other toads and frogs. As has been mentioned, the female midwife toad produces three or four egg strings in succession—four strings in the case of somewhat older females—so there were several water matings. Kammerer reported that he returned a thoroughly readjusted pair of midwife toads to a cooler terrarium where they could have mated on land. But the new (or rather the reawakened old) habit proved stronger and they went into the water for mating.

All this corresponded with the work done by Marie von Chauvin with the axolotl. It proved that the midwife toad was still capable, under some external pressure of circumstances, to resume what we take to have been its original mode of life. But Kammerer went further; he reported that the tadpoles produced by the water matings went on land when they were ready and grew up on land. But when mating time came they returned to the water! Moreover, Kammerer reported, at least one male also acquired new physical characteristics. The males of normally water-mating toads have something like small warts near the "thumbs" of their forefeet; the purpose of these is to help the male hold on to the female, and they are therefore called "nuptial pads." On

land nuptial pads are not needed and the male midwife toad
does not have them, but in the process of a large number of
water matings one male developed them.

But before I continue this particular story I must return
to the other animal on which Kammerer was working,
Salamandra maculosa. In Europe, where it is common, it is
also known by the popular name of fire salamander, presumably with reference to mythical-alchemical legends about
the salamander that can live in (and is the spirit of) fire. Its
appearance can readily reinforce such ideas. It is a fairly
small salamander, 4 to 5 inches in total length, and the main
color of its skin is black, the shiny deep black of patent
leather. Scattered over this shiny black skin are large, sharply
outlined spots of an equally shiny yellow. The salamander
looks as if yellow paint had dripped on it, an impression
which is heightened by the complete randomness of the spots.
As a last item of this short description I might add that
the fire salamander always manages to look well nourished.

A color scheme like that of *Salamandra maculosa* is the
precise opposite of camouflage. It has been called "warning
coloration," and other names to the same effect. Such coloration, translated into human speech, means: "You'll be sorry
if you eat me," because it is accompanied by an abominable
taste or even outright poison. The point is that a color scheme
which does not hide the wearer but actually advertises his
presence has nothing to do with environment and should
not be influenced by environment in any manner. But
Kammerer proceeded to prove that it was—he would not
accept the idea that something might not be influenced by
environment. He kept generations of salamanders on black
top soil and other generations on yellow soil. According to
his reports, in the salamanders kept on black top soil the size
of the yellow spots was reduced, and this reduction was passed
on by inheritance. In the salamanders kept on yellow soil
the size of the black areas was reduced, and that too was
passed on. Kammerer then stated that he noticed that the

yellow soil he used tended to retain more moisture than did
the black soil; he then found through another series of generations of salamanders that greater moisture increased the
size of the yellow spots, even if the soil did not have a particular color.

Personally he was more interested in the blackening of his
experimental animals, which apparently was easier to accomplish; at any event his own pictures of specimens of extremes
show that the black areas on a "yellow" specimen were much

The European "fire salamander," *Salamandra maculosa*

larger than the remaining yellow spots on a "black" specimen. In the end he claimed that he had succeeded in making
a *Salamandra maculosa* over into a *Salamandra atra*, a relative of the fire salamander which is usually called the black
Alpine salamander, and is about the same size, but all black
in color and much more slender in build.

Other scientists sat back in astonishment. The pigmented
olms were one thing, the midwife toad with nuptial pads was
already a different story, but the converted salamanders began
to verge on the incredible. But there was no reason to doubt
Kammerer's word, which, after all, was the word of a member

of a reliable scientific institution. This still left the possibility that a mistake had been made somewhere—I'm not talking about the crucial and hotly debated question of interpretation but about the experiments themselves. One researcher, reading carefully through the long series of reports in search of a hidden mistake, suddenly made another kind of discovery. If you added the generations of experimental animals you could arrive at the time required for the study, with a negligible margin of error. But it did not jibe with the time Kammerer, according to his own records, had been at work.

Scientists in various countries began to demand explanations and exhibits of evidence. They wanted to see the specimen of *Salamandra atra* which had come from many generations of *maculosa,* and they wanted to see a live specimen, not something in a jar. They wanted to see, especially, the midwife toad with the nuptial pads. One scientist, William Bateson, attacked Kammerer sharply. The normal response would have been to invite Professor Bateson and other witnesses and show the evidence. For seven years Paul Kammerer evaded any attempt at examining his specimens. Finally, in 1926, the male midwife toad (by that time dead and preserved in alcohol) was carefully examined by Dr. G. Kingsley Noble of the American Museum of Natural History (New York) and by Dr. Hans Przibram of the University of Vienna, the director of the institute where Kammerer worked. The midwife toad had distinct nuptial pads, but they had been made by injections of India ink!

Noble and Przibram published separate reports on the investigation in *Nature* of August 7, 1926. On September 22, 1926, Kammerer wrote a long and rather confused letter to the Moscow Academy of Science[5] in which he said that after

[5] Kammerer was apparently in such a state that he did not even remember the proper name of the institute to which he wrote and to which he bequeathed his library. His letter was addressed "To the Presidium of the Communist Academy, Moscow" and began with the words: "Respected Comrades and Colleagues."

having read the "attack upon me made by Dr. Noble in *Nature*," he went to examine his specimens himself. "I found the statements of Dr. Noble completely verified. Indeed there were still other objects (blackened salamanders) upon which my results had plainly been 'improved' post mortem with India ink." A few days after mailing this letter Kammerer committed suicide.

"American biologists," Professor Conway Zirkle wrote later in his book, *Death of a Science in Russia*, "as a whole have tended to excuse Kammerer (*de mortuis nil nisi bonum*) and blame some overzealous assistant who wanted to give the master what the master so obviously wanted. Such things have been known to happen. Before we can accept this charitable interpretation, however, we shall have to explain Kammerer's seven-year reluctance to have his specimen examined, and his prolonged and skillful evasions of his critics' demands."

Professor Richard B. Goldschmidt, a scientist who knew Kammerer personally, does not believe in the "helpful assistant" theory, either. In an article published in *Science* for March 4, 1949, he wrote (p. 221):

Very likely there are few men left who knew Kammerer and who had seen his work in Vienna under his own guidance, so I should like to give my interpretation of this much-discussed tragedy. I do not believe that Kammerer was an intentional forger. He was a very high-strung, decadent but brilliant man who spent his nights, after a day in the laboratory, composing symphonies. He was originally not a scientist but an *Aquarianer,* an amateur breeder of lower vertebrates. In this field he had an immense skill, and I believe that the data he presented upon the direct action of the environment are largely correct. (Some of them were actually anticipated a long time before in Weismann's laboratory by M. von Chauvin, who made the experiments for just the opposite reason.) He then conceived the idea that he could prove the inheritance of acquired characters and became so obsessed with this idea that he "improved" upon his records. I have reason to believe, from what I have seen in his laboratory, that he continued his experiments, which ended by the death of the specimens, by starting again with similar-looking animals. His Aquarianer mind did not consider this wrong. He simply did not know what an experiment amounted to. In later years he probably became so absorbed with the necessity of proving his claims that he started inventing results or "doctoring" them. Though the actual results of all this amounted to falsification, I am not certain that he realized it and intended it. He probably was a nervous wreck in the end.[6]

The subsequent events took place, as is quite suitable, considering the theme, in a different "environment." The scene shifted from laboratories, learned journals, and scientific seminars to political meetings, the daily press, and totalitarian propaganda factories.

Some time before Kammerer died, he had received an invitation from the Soviet Union to come to Russia as a refugee from "bourgeois persecution." Nobody knows why he did not accept. But since he did not, Anatoli Vassilyevitch Lunatcharski, then Commissar of Education, decided that Lunatcharski, then Commissar of Education, decided that the dead Kammerer could at least be used as a political martyr.

Marxism originated with *Das Kapital*, Volume I, in 1867. Evolutionary thought had received its firm foundation with *The Origin of Species* in 1859. That Marxism embraced evolutionary ideas early in its career is not surprising, for science showed here that kings and peasants, capitalists and day laborers all had once been something which for the sake of brevity was called "monkey." I remember reading a pamphlet, which from its appearance must have been printed around 1900, possibly earlier, containing the sentence: "If the one-million-year-ago ancestor of Napoleon III and the

[6] Some time after reading this article I asked Professor Goldschmidt whether he had ever seen Kammerer's olm with eyes. Professor Goldschmidt replied: "He [Kammerer] showed me one specimen with normal eyes. If he had not transplanted different eyes it agreed with his claims. The thing should be repeated!" (Letter dated September 19, 1950.) My own impression, after much reading about and by Kammerer, is that the olm experiments were honest and genuine, but that, as Professor Goldschmidt said, the thing should be repeated. The illustration on page 21 is drawn after Kammerer's own photograph.

one-million-year-ago ancestor of his washerwoman were alive
now we'd put them both in the same cage in the zoo." Up to
this point the political reasoning is clear. But when science
began to go into detail about the probable mechanism of
evolution, Marxism picked Lamarckism (without the name)
as the concept that must be "right." Presumably the reasoning was this: if one had to accept Darwin's ideas, or the
mutations observed by De Vries, one could never predict
where genius might strike. One also might have to wait endlessly. But if everything depended on environment, it was a
different story. Marxism, once in power, could and would
manipulate environment and thereby not only guide additional evolution but speed it up too. I can't tell what other
thoughts may have influenced the decision, but as time went
by Marxism, or at least Russian Marxism, insisted more and
more firmly that there *must* be inheritance of acquired characteristics. And in Russia Marxism could manipulate the
environment at least to the extent of having this theory
taught to students.

Commissar of Education Lunatcharski was also in charge
of motion-picture production. It so happened that his wife
was an actress, an intelligent and exceptionally beautiful
woman. The commissar himself wrote the script for a film,
in which he included a nice big role for his beautiful wife
and a minor role for himself, that of Commissar of Education. The title of the film was *Salamandra*.

The action of the movie takes place in a "central European
university town," but not in Vienna. Some of the sequences
were photographed in Erfurt, which did have a university
from 1392 until 1816. At the fictional university there works
a young professor who devotes all his spare time, not to the
composing of symphonies, but to the welfare of the common
people. In his working hours he breeds *Salamandra maculosa*,
influencing their coloration by environment. One day he
achieves success; the changes prove to be inherited. The
bishop of the cathedral—here the film showed the actual

Beatae Mariae Virginis cathedral of Erfurt—immediately
learns of the discovery, since the young professor makes no
secret of his work. Equally immediately the bishop realizes
that the professor's discovery means the end of the power and
influence of the church—don't ask me why it should or would.
The bishop thereupon summons a royal prince (the movie
obviously meant the eldest son of the German Crown Prince,
who at that time was in America working for Henry Ford)
to the church. They meet in the middle of the night—again
I don't know why—and the bishop turns out to have arranged
at an earlier date that the prince be appointed assistant to the
professor. The next day the assistant suggests to the professor
that he should announce his discovery at a formal meeting
of the university. When the professor agrees, the prince and
the bishop sneak into the laboratory (again at night), open
the jar containing the specimen, and inject the animal with
India ink.

Next day the whole university is assembled, with the faculty
in ceremonial robes, and the young professor makes a re-
sounding speech. After the speech the proof specimen is
exhibited. In front of everybody the villain dips it in water
and the dark color runs out with a rapidity that can be
accomplished only on film. The professor is dismissed with
equal rapidity and virtually at once appears on the streets in
ragged clothing, begging with the aid of a rhesus monkey,
originally an experimental animal, who had followed the
professor into poverty and disgrace. Then one of his former
students arrives in town—yes, Madame Lunatcharskaya herself; she had so filled the screen before that nobody could
fail to recognize her at a glance—looking for her old teacher.
She finally locates him in a bare, cold, and leaking attic, and
after learning what has happened takes the next train to
Moscow and asks for an interview with the Commissar of
Education (which she gets about as speedily as she would
have in reality, being his wife). The Commissar issues orders
to save the poor young professor. The former student goes

back in person, arrives in time to prevent the professor from committing suicide, and they board a train for Moscow which is greeted at the border by peasants with banners extolling the land of liberty and the inheritance of acquired characteristics.

The conclusion of the real story is completely Russian—the movie had prophesied correctly to that extent. With official policy firmly established in *Salamandra*, it was now easy to label the "wrong" doctrines. All one had to do was to use the names of those scientists who did not think that acquired characteristics could be inherited. To believe in "Weismannism" was very wrong and "Morganism" (after Nobel Prize-winning American geneticist Thomas Hunt Morgan) was just as bad. Gregor Mendel, who discovered the laws of heredity, was another villain (and he had been a churchman to boot). But while there were all these "enemies," there was no shining example for quite some time. Lamarck, the logical alternate to Darwin, was not publicized, or even mentioned; maybe because he had been the Chevalier de Lamarck.

Quite late the Russians "discovered" Ivan Vladimirovitch Mitchurin and named "Mitchurinism" after him. To non-Russians his name was simply unknown. He seems to have been a man very much like Luther Burbank, except that he received very little publicity in his lifetime. What Mitchurin did or did not do is actually rather unimportant; his name became the all-inclusive label for everything that was "right" in genetics, in contrast to "Weismannism-Morganism" which was the label for everything "wrong."

If Mitchurin was the guiding light, the prophet of the truth was Trofím Denisovitch Lysenko. He defended "Mitchurinism" and his own views—expressed in political terms—against the views of the older Russian scientists who had merely spent a lifetime of hard work. Lysenko's trump card was a very simple one. After a critical meeting, at which written questions were asked, he announced that one question had been whether his ideas had the approval of the

Central Committee of the Communist Party. Yes, he said, they do have the approval of the Central Committee. Whereupon the men who up to that moment had thought that Weismann and Morgan and others had worked hard and produced results knew that they had to agree with Lysenko, that they had to recant in public or resign and await what might happen to them.

As for Lysenko's views, it is hard to tell what they are. He did not, or does not, believe in the existence of genes; hence those who do (and photograph them with the electron microscope) are "idealists," which in Russia is a harsh term of disapproval. He does think that the environment will change heredity and that a radical change in environment will "shatter" heredity so that entirely new forms must appear. He claimed, for example, that such shattered heredity had converted wheat into rye. But mostly he pulled political strings.

After several years of virtual omnipotence of the great (or at least greatly publicized) Trofím Denisovitch Lysenko there came a sudden sharp turn. Iosif Vissarionovitch Djugashvili, known as Stalin, died. And barely six weeks later Russian scientists suddenly attacked Lysenko in such official publications as the *Journal of General Biology* (an organ of the Soviet Academy of Sciences) and called him a "falsifier of evidence," which is, of course, merely the plain truth. Lysenko then stated publicly that he had worked out his theories with Stalin's "aid." A little later he amended the statement by saying that certain portions had been "dictated to him by Stalin almost verbatim."

The story ends here. But I am afraid only temporarily. While Georgi Malenkov was premier of Soviet Russia, opposing scientists could say whatever they thought right about Lysenko. But Malenkov was ousted by Khrushchev, who promptly took Lysenko back into favor and put him in charge of increasing grain production.

The future of the controversy about the inheritance of acquired characteristics is likely to be interesting, to say the least.

2: The Little People

TAKE a map of the North American continent and look for Hudson Bay. It connects with the Atlantic Ocean to the east by way of Hudson Strait, which, on the inland side, ends at a large island: Southampton Island. To the north of Southampton Island you'll find Foxe Channel, to the east of Foxe Channel the Foxe Peninsula, which is a part of Baffin Island. To the north of Foxe Channel, finally, there is Foxe Basin. As the spelling suggests, these names have nothing to do with an arctic variety of the well-known carnivore but are derived from the name of a man: Captain Luke Foxe of Hull, who explored this region in 1631 and 1632. Like many another sailor of his time he tried to find the so-called North-West Passage through which, it was hoped, one could sail into the Pacific Ocean across the northern part of North America.

When Captain Luke Foxe published the journal of his voyage (in 1635) the book bore the title

NORTH-VVEST FOX;
or Fox from the North-west Passage

Much later it was reprinted by the Hakluyt Society as volume 88/89 of its publications. On page 319 of the second volume of the Hakluyt Society edition there is mention of an island which had just been visited by an exploring party:

The newes from the land was that this Iland was a Sepulchre, for that the Salvages had laid their dead (I cannot say interred), for it is all stone, as they cannot dig therein, but lay the Corpes upon the stones, and well them about with the same, coffining them also by laying the sides of old sleddes above, which have been artificially made. The boards are some 9 or 10 ft long, 4 inches thicke. In what manner the tree they have bin made out of was cloven or sawen, it was so smooth as we could not discerne, the burials had been so old. And, as in other places of those countries, they bury all their Vtensels, as bowes, arrowes, strings, darts, lances, and other implements carved in bone. The longest Corpes was not above 4 foot long, with their heads laid to the West.

The printed book does not say more about this most astonishing find, except for stating that "their Corpes were wrapped in Deare skinnes" and that the sailors left them undisturbed, but took the wooden boards for firewood. But a hand-written copy of the original manuscript contains an additional sentence: "They seem to be people of small stature, God send me better for my adventures than these."

This, I am sorry to say, is all that is known about the case of the stony graves of "little people" in the Western Hemisphere. Captain Foxe wrote that "this Iland doth lie in 64 d. 10 m. of latitude," but there is no island in this geographical position. There are, however, a number of small islands at the southern end of Foxe Channel, any one of which may be meant. Of course one can disbelieve the whole story and be done with it; but it is hard to see why Captain Foxe should have inserted a few paragraphs of completely useless lies in an otherwise trustworthy narrative. If he did tell the truth, he is the only witness to the only known case of "little people" in the Americas.

Of course every country has its own legends and stories about "little people." Details vary, but always, in addition to being small, these people are described as living either deep in the forest or else in caves in the mountains. The folklore of some countries includes both types of habitat and provides different names; German folklore, for example, distinguishes between the gnomes who live *in* the mountains (not *on* the mountains) and the *Ellenmännchen* of the forest. The latter term is virtually self-translating; all that needs to be added is that, while the English "ell" was standardized early as being 3 feet in length like the yard, elsewhere an ell was usually somewhat longer—about 4 feet.

How the "little people" got into folklore is by no means certain, but the fact that there exists a long literary tradition about them no doubt helped. Anybody who asked the learned men of his time about the gnomes and the ell-men did receive confirmation of some kind, since small-sized people had been mentioned in various highly regarded works that had been preserved from the classical age. Herodotus, the "Father of History," told in the second book of his work about an adventure of five Nasamonians which had been related to him in Egypt. Five young men of this tribe decided to learn something firsthand about the unknown parts of Africa.

After journeying for many days over a wide extent of sand, they came at last to a plain where they observed trees growing; approaching them and seeing fruit on them, they proceeded to gather it. While they were thus engaged, there came upon them some dwarfish men, under the middle height, who seized them and carried them off. The Nasamonians could not understand a word of their language, nor had they any acquaintance with the language of the Nasamonians. They were led across extensive marshes, and finally came to a town, where all the men were of the height of their conductors, and black complexioned. A great river [probably the Niger] flowed by the town, running from west to east, and containing crocodiles.

But the literary tradition about the "little people" had begun even earlier than Herodotus, with Homer's *Iliad*, which acquired its final shape in about 600 B.C., or possibly earlier. The hexameters of lines 3-7 of the third book of the *Iliad* read:

> Like to the unending screeching of cranes which fly overhead then
> When, having fled from the unceasing rains and the cold of the
>   winter,
> Screaming they fly down the path to Okéanos' far-flowing waters,
> Threatening death and destruction to races of small-bodied
>   pygmies,
> Swooping on down from the high dusky air to do terrible
>   combat. . . .

Egyptian or Cretan sailors must have told that somewhere, far to the south and almost at the rim of the world, there lived "small-bodied pygmies." To those who might be distrustful of a poet's assertion the *Natural History* of Aristotle served nicely:

> The cranes fly from the Scythian plains [Russia] to the swamps situated beyond Upper Egypt, whence the Nile comes. These areas are inhabited by pygmies. This is no myth, there actually exists a small tribe, and even their horses are small, their habits are said to be those of Troglodites [cave dwellers].

Later, in Europe, Homer was not known directly but people did know Aristotle, and also Pliny who had copied that paragraph from Aristotle. An amusing side-thought cropped up later in the writings of Albert von Bollstädt (Albertus Magnus) in the thirteenth century. After quoting Aristotle, he adds that the pygmies stand one ell tall, that they have children when they are three years old, and that they die in their eighth year. After stating this, he suddenly paused to ask *utrum pygmaei sint homines?* (whether the pygmies are people?). His answer is a firm "no." They can speak and presumably think, but they merely live together without forming a community; they have neither art nor philosophy, neither a moral code nor decency. Although they can make things they are not people. Since Albertus cannot have known such details (and since, moreover, his assertions are wrong on every count), all this must be the result of "pure thought." But his reasoning certainly became food for German folklore: the ell-men can speak and practice some crafts, but pictures awe and worry them, and they are not people because they lack immortal souls.

It is difficult to imagine what a scientist of, say, the first half of the eighteenth century might have answered when asked about the pygmies. Most likely he would have asserted that they were merely folklore—Greek, Egyptian, Latin, and European—which was helped along by an occasional midget, a freak born to normal parents and having normal offspring, if any.[1] But during the latter half of the eighteenth century some stories, emanating mostly from Portugal, began making the rounds. Portuguese sailors, returning from Africa, swore that they had been told by reliable Negroes about "little men" in the forest, and "hairy men" in the forest, and "big hairy men" in the mountains. All this remained rumor, possibly true but most likely not, for another century.

The man who furnished the first definite proof was born on July 31, 1835, in France, probably in Paris. His name was Paul Belloni du Chaillu and he came to the United States when he was twenty years old. Because he already had some African experience the Academy of Natural Sciences in Philadelphia sent him on an expedition to equatorial West Africa. On this expedition du Chaillu discovered the gorilla, once and for all time ending the ancient confusion between gorilla and chimpanzee. (The latter had been called "gorilla" and the real gorilla had been thought mythical.) Naturally such a successful man was sent on another expedition, which he later described in a book called *Journey to Ashangoland*. On that expedition, made during the years 1863-65, du Chaillu encountered the pygmies. They were of the tribe of

---

[1] I remember reading somewhere (and quite some time ago) that a king of France once tried to establish a "tribe" of small people by caring for a number of midgets and generally unusual small people, on condition that they would marry and have children. They did, but the result was disappointing—almost all their children "grew up."

the Obongo, and du Chaillu reported that apparently they
were not "real Negroes." Their skin was neither dark brown
nor black, but a pale yellow-brown, "like imperfectly roasted
coffee beans." They did not have much beard and not much
hair on their heads, but "a great growth of body hair," especially when contrasted with the neighboring Negro tribes,
which have virtually none, much less than even a relatively
hairless white man. Of course he measured them, and found
the average height of the males 4 feet, 7 inches, the females
some 6 inches shorter.

Du Chaillu's discovery settled the question of whether
pygmies existed at all, but it did not clear up the problem of
the pygmies mentioned by Homer and Aristotle. *They* were
supposed to live in or beyond the Nile swamps, somewhere
near the Mountains of the Moon, and not in West Africa.
Geographers had already settled the problem of the Mountains of the Moon by the time du Chaillu made his voyages.
High mountains had been discovered in equatorial Africa;
the ancients probably meant the ones now known as the
Ruwenzori range. And a linguist had also found the explanation for the intriguing and ancient name "Mountains of
the Moon." In Arabic this is *Jibal el-qamar,* but what the
Arabs had said and written originally was *Jibal qomr,* meaning "bluish [distant?] mountains."

To establish the "classical" pygmies was the lot of a German, Dr. Georg August Schweinfurth, who was born in Riga
on December 29, 1836. Schweinfurth, a gifted artist and an
ardent student of plant life, followed a course which could
be expected to lead him to the sources of the Nile. He penetrated the territory of the Niam-niam, discovered the Welle
River and established that it was not a tributary of the Nile,
and, in 1870, saw his first pygmy.

This was Adimokoo of the tribe of the Akka, a fairly old
man and rather tall—4 feet, 10 inches. Schweinfurth had
read du Chaillu's books and knew of the Obongo. His Akka
seemed to be about the same size; they had the same skin

color; but they did not have more body hair than their tall neighbors. Their physical proportions were not extraordinary: they were slightly short-legged, especially when compared with the usually long-legged Negroes; they had a tendency to a "pendulous abdomen" and rather large shell-like ears. Schweinfurth stressed that point as indicative of a racial difference, because "all Negroes have beautiful ears." Adimokoo, questioned with the aid of interpreters, rattled off the names of seven other pygmy tribes. Schweinfurth's notes and sketches were destroyed later when his camp caught fire, but he remembered having measured a male Akka who was only 4 feet, 4 inches, tall and a female Akka 4 feet, 1 inch.

In spite of Aristotle's two mistakes about these pygmies—they are not cave dwellers and they don't have horses, either large or small—they are undoubtedly the ones he meant, as is indicated by the fact that they were known to the Egyptians. The Cairo Museum preserves an old (but ap-

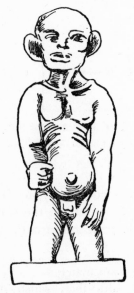

Ancient Egyptian statuette of a pygmy, in the Cairo Museum

parently undated) statuette of a typical pygmy, and three
pygmies appear on a frieze in the Festival Hall of Osorkon II
in the Temple of Bubastis. In addition to this pictorial evidence we have direct information from the Sixth Dynasty.
An Egyptian named Harkhuf had traveled south to "Nubia"

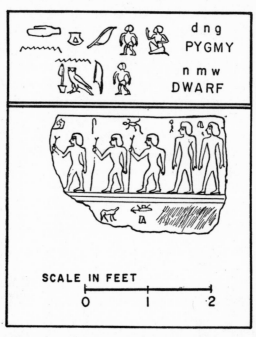

A frieze from the Festival Hall of Osorkon II in the Temple of Bubastis,
showing three pygmies. *Above,* the hieroglyphs for "dwarf" and
for "pygmy"

repeatedly, and on his fourth trip he secured a pygmy. This
was important enough information to be sent to the ruling
pharaoh, who immediately dispatched an enthusiastic and
detailed letter to the traveler.

Come northward to the Residence immediately. . . . Leave
[everything?] and bring this pygmy with thee, which thou
hast brought living, prosperous, and healthy from the land of

Akhtin [unknown southern people] for the dances of the god to rejoice and gladden the heart of the King of Upper and Lower Egypt Neferkerē, may [he] live forever. When he [i.e., the pygmy] goes down with thee to the vessel, appoint trusty people who shall be about him on each side of the vessel; take care lest he fall into the water. When he sleeps at night, appoint again trusty people who shall sleep about him in his tent: inspect ten times a night. My Majesty desires to see this pygmy more than the produce of Sinai and of Pwenet. If thou arrivest at the Residence, this pygmy bring with thee alive, prosperous, and healthy, My Majesty will do for thee a greater thing than that which was done for the Treasurer of the god Werdjedba in the time of Isesi, in accordance with the heart's desire of My Majesty to see this pygmy.

Harkhuf must have been successful in bringing the pygmy "alive, prosperous, and healthy" to the Residence, because he himself was later prosperous enough to have the ruler's letter reproduced on his tomb—which is how we know about it.[2]

Hard on the heels of Schweinfurth's report came some detailed information about Asiatic pygmy tribes, the earliest mention of which was in the famous, though mutilated and fragmentary book of Ctesias, the personal physician of Artaxerxes II. The ones about which Ctesias had heard were probably the forest pygmies of the Malayan peninsula; the pygmy-like natives of the Andaman Islands, the Aētes of the Philippine Islands, and others were discovered much later.

Anthropologists now call the African pygmy tribes Negrillos, and the Asiatic tribes Negritos. The distribution of the Negrillos and Negritos on a map of the world is spotty in detail, but the general features of this distribution can be easily described. It is all Old World, from Africa around to the Philippines, generally between the equator and 20 de-

[2] Some of the representations on Egyptian tombs and other monuments which have been referred to as pygmies in literature are actually dwarfs, midgets. The Egyptians distinguished between the two; there were different words and different symbols for them.

grees northern latitude. In all cases the pygmies live in unde-
sirable surroundings, usually in dense forests, though some
of the island Negritos are obvious exceptions. It certainly
looks as if they had been pushed into areas which their taller
and stronger neighbors did not covet for themselves. As soon
as that fact was realized a question came up which sounds
rather like a conscious paraphrase of Albertus Magnus. But
the question was no longer whether the pygmies are people;
that had been settled. It was now whether the pygmies
might not be the "original people." Did they by any chance
represent the early human stock, now scattered and pushed
into odd corners, surviving in small and generally browbeaten leftovers?

Scientists toying with this idea around the year 1910 recalled to themselves and to their audiences that the ancestors
of the horse had been much smaller than present-day horses,
and that, in general, most large mammals of today had
smaller ancestors. Why should this not apply to people too,
especially in view of the fact that all our living, though distant, relatives are far smaller than Man, with the single
exception of the gorilla? It was a nice and logical idea which
suffered only from one serious drawback: it was not supported by fossil evidence anywhere.

At that time a number of human fossils were already
known. There was the famous Neanderthal skull, found in
1856 in the Neander Valley, a short distance above the Düssel
River and not far from the industrial city of Düsseldorf.
That Neanderthal skull, after a long-drawn-out and rather
silly controversy, had finally been accepted as human. Its
owner was not particularly tall, as proved by later and more
complete finds. He stood around 5 feet, 3 inches, to 5 feet,
4 inches—not very tall as present averages go, but certainly
not a pygmy.

Then there was the "Heidelberg jaw," found on October
21, 1907, in a sand pit near the town of Mauer, not far from
Heidelberg. Its owner is still unknown as far as complete

skeletons go, but two things about him were realized within weeks of the discovery itself. He was considerably earlier than "Neanderthal" and he was a big man. Recent estimates say about 6 feet, 2 inches, with a probable leeway of 2 inches in either direction. Certainly not a pygmy.

And there was *Pithecanthropus,* from Trinil on Java, found in 1891 by the Dutch physician Dr. Eugène Dubois. Only a skull cap and a femur were found, and for a long time it was doubtful whether they belonged together or not. But either way you took it *Pithecanthropus* worked out to be over 5 feet. No matter what else he was, he was well within the size range of modern Man.

In addition to all these forms, which differed considerably from modern Man in many particulars, there were the Crô-Magnon, later than Neanderthal and no doubt the direct ancestors of many Europeans. The name comes from the place of the supposed first discovery in 1868, Crô-Magnon at Les Eyzies, Departement de Dordogne, France. It later turned out that these Crô-Magnon had been discovered before. In 1823 Dean Buckland of Oxford University had unearthed a fine skeleton from the Paviland Cave, on the seaward side of Bristol Channel, England. He had thought it to be the skeleton of a Briton lady of the Roman period and because it was stained with red ochre it was later referred to as the "Red Lady." In 1912 the Abbé Breuil examined it carefully and found his suspicions correct: the "Red Lady" was a Crô-Magnon, and male at that. And in 1852 a small landslide near the village of Aurignac, France, had exposed a cave in which the skeletons of seventeen persons were found. The mayor of Aurignac was informed about this, looked at them, regretted the accident which had overtaken the party of indubitably nice people, and laid the case before the local abbé. They were given a Christian burial, of which the victims of an accident are deserving. They were Crô-Magnon too, the men averaging 6 feet, 1 inch (some taller), the women around 5 feet, 7 inches.

In 1921, at Broken Hill, Northern Rhodesia, a skeleton generally resembling the Neanderthal type was found. This man's weight, when he was alive, must have been around 210 pounds, and he must have stood 5 feet, 10 inches, tall. His case also spoiled some contentions about the degenerate state of modern people, whose appendixes act up, whose teeth decay, and whose little toes are being reduced because of their habit of wearing shoes. We don't know about the appendix and the little toe of *Homo rhodesiensis,* but he must have had toothaches which surpassed description. He had a mastoid breakthrough, too, and literally died of the septic condition of his mouth.

But no pygmies had been found anywhere.

There had been a loud noise emanating from Switzerland in about 1910 concerning whole villages of pygmies from the period of the Late Stone Age. The noise had been all the louder because the artifacts had become somebody's private property and were commercially exploited. But a Swiss anthropologist, Dr. Franz Schwerz of Berne, had traced everything still available and found that the men had been 5 feet, 3 inches, on the average, and the women 4 feet, 11 inches. While he was at it he also determined the average size of the Late Stone Age populations of France and of Denmark, finding it in France 5 feet, 5½ inches, for the males and 5 feet, 1 inch, for the females, and in Denmark 5 feet, 7 inches, for the males and 5 feet, 5 inches, for the females. These sets of figures were still approximately correct for the populations of the two countries in 1914 when he made his study.

Just as a scientist in 1814 would have been highly skeptical about the existence of living pygmies, in spite of some rumors, so a scientist of 1914 had every reason to be highly skeptical about the existence of prehistoric pygmies. But the rumors would not die. Prehistoric Man had not become known only because of his bones. One might almost say, on the contrary. The first indications of his existence had been

the tools he had made, the now so well-known flint implements of early Man. They had come to light piecemeal all
through recorded history, the first to guess at their meaning
being a British antiquary named John Frere. That was in
1797, but it was another half-century before everybody had

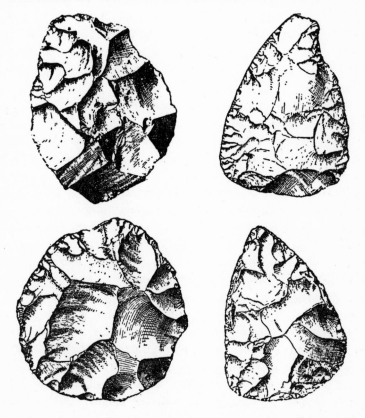

Undoubted stone tools of primitive Man, found at various sites in France

become used to the simple concept that Man, before he
learned how to smelt and work metals, made his tools and
weapons of stones.

As more and more material was amassed, scientists first
distinguished between the "Old" and the "New" Stone Age,

the implements from the "New" Stone Age being far superior in workmanship. Later this scheme had to be broken
down further, into types of weapons and into localities—
there were regional differences even then. But all stone
implements, whether "old" or "new," came from the same
geological period, the period immediately preceding our
own, which is known as either the Pleistocene or the Ice Age.
The latter name is not quite as good as the former, for the
big glaciations from which the term Ice Age came comprised
only a comparatively small portion of the total time of the
Pleistocene.

But along with the collections of primitive stone implements a kind of small side collection began to form. If the
artifacts which comprised this side collection had been
found in any of the deposits which could be dated as having
been the "interglacial periods," the long stretches of time
between the glaciations, there would have been very little
fuss about them. They would have been taken as belonging
to a very primitive tribe, one which even the gentleman from
the Neander Valley would consider far beneath his notice
(except as food) and that with justification. Or they might
have been considered the first attempts of an apprentice boy,
learning the craft; or discarded pieces, just begun when an
interruption took place and not recovered afterward. As
these remarks indicate, they show very little workmanship,
so little that a layman would hardly think they had been
worked on at all. Even the experts are often doubtful, and
some of the pieces, as some of the experts claim, may have
been chipped accidentally by natural causes. Their whole
relationship to Man may consist in having been stepped on
once by somebody.

But these pieces are *not* from the Pleistocene. They are
from deposits of the Tertiary Period, with a minimum age
of one million years. They have been called "eoliths" (dawn
stones) and will be fought over for many years to come. What
is important here is that some, found by Professor Rutot of

Brussels, are not only old but also small. Professor Rutot sent some of them to a German naturalist, the late Wilhelm Bölsche, who, in reply to a question, wrote me that one thing is absolutely certain: *If* the eoliths which he had in his col-

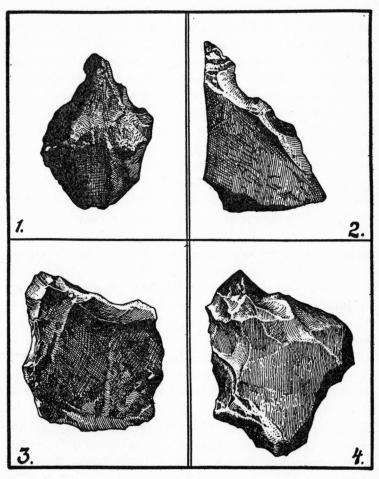

"Eoliths"

Of these four stones, two (2 and 4) are known to be stone tools, fashioned within historic times by the now extinct Tasmanians. The other two, similar in general appearance, are "eoliths" from Europe

lection actually were tools they were made for the hands of small children or pygmies. And he, as well as Rutot, felt sure that the marks they bore were not accidental but the result of admittedly primitive and clumsy workmanship. Now, as is discussed in Chapter 3, it is well known that some animals use "tools." As almost any zoo visitor must have seen on occasion, monkeys use stones to crack open nuts—or to throw at other monkeys, the beginnings of missile warfare. But whether the use is peaceful or hostile in intent, the monkeys use the stones as they find them. They don't do anything to them to make them more efficient; they do not use one tool to improve another tool. Since this is so, it was only natural for Bölsche to add in his letter the statement that he would rather believe that in Belgium during the Miocene (one of the subdivisions of the Tertiary Period) there lived a small ape who had progressed to improved tools, than consider the chip marks on these eoliths accidental.

Considering the age of the dawn stones, his is probably the only explanation, unless Rutot dated his finds wrongly, or unless the chip marks really are accidental, in spite of expert opinion.

In addition to these doubtful and violently debated eoliths, Belgium produced another find along the same lines. During the last year of the First World War a German professor from the University of Göttingen discovered something near Antwerp which he claimed was a human footprint. Unfortunately it was not one of these nice clear prints like those left for posterity by dinosaurs. The "print" consisted of five fragments, some of which had been as much as 30 feet apart when found. The date, according to Professor Freudenberg, must be about the same as that of the disputed eoliths, around the middle of the Tertiary Period. The fragments do not fit together and one of them was broken when found and had to be cemented together. Two of them Freudenberg himself called "doubtful," numbers 3 and 5 in the illustration. The others *may* show the imprint of the

big toe, the little toe, and the ball of the foot; and you don't
have to be a case-hardened skeptic to call the last one doubtful too. From the size of the big toe—if that is what it is—the

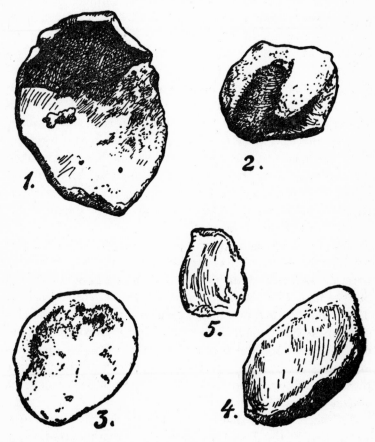

The fragments found by Professor Freudenberg near Antwerp in Belgium and explained by him as the remains of a footprint of a human
being from the Tertiary Period

Fragment "1" is said to be the impression of the ball of the foot (the black line
shows where the two pieces, found 10 yards apart, were cemented together);
"2," the imprint of the little toe and portion of the imprint of the toe next to
it; "4" might be the imprint of the big toe; while "3" and "5" are considered
"questionable" by Freudenberg himself

discoverer calculated that its owner stood 30 inches tall; the calculation must have involved so many assumptions that it cannot be considered proof of any kind.

But we do have some genuine and complete footprints of prehistoric Man. A fairly recent discovery of a large number of human footprints from the Ice Age—the period of the last glaciation—was widely publicized. The discoverer was the Abbé Cathala, who found the prints in a side cave of the Grotto of Aldène in southern France which had been overlooked by earlier explorers. The age could be determined rather well—it is between 15,000 and 20,000 years. The people who made the prints carried staffs and torches—there are marks on the walls where the torches were rubbed for cleaning them. Some pictures of these prints were published in *Life* magazine, December 6, 1948. But the newspapers were wrong in saying that these were the first prehistoric footprints discovered.

The first had been found, also in France, in 1912. The place of the discovery was the cave called the Tuc d'Audoubert, situated near Saint Girons on the estates of the Comte de Bégouen. The discoverers were the count's teen-aged sons. They found a cave in which prehistoric men had made clay sculptures with enough artistry to stand even tough present-day competition. The material was clay, scooped up in an adjoining cave. And that clay, where it was scooped up, showed handprints and footprints, deep impressions, covered with a thin veneer of lime.

All the books say that these prints of the Salle de Danse, as this cave of the Tuc d'Audoubert has been named because of the footprints, are "small and delicate," but none I read gave any measurements. Of the new prints in the Grotto of Aldène the measurements were provided by Norbert Casteret in Saint Gaudens. The length of a step, he wrote, where it can be established, is 50 centimeters (about 20 inches); the length of the footprints varies from 18 to 25 centimeters (between 7 and 10 inches). The little toe shows signs of reduction, to the same extent as that of modern Man. Like the septic teeth of *Homo rhodesiensis*, this demolishes another tenet of those who warn of degeneration and doom; the Aldène people did not wear shoes, as we can clearly see. How tall were they?

Since they are rather modern we can assume that their proportions were about the same as ours. Among white people of today there is a well-known relationship between foot length and height. Males, we find, are between 6 and 6.5 times as tall as their footprint is long. Among women the variation is somewhat greater; it usually lies between the figures 6.5 and 7, but some especially long-legged and small-footed individuals may be almost 7.5 times as tall as the length of their footprints.

Taking the largest of the Aldène footprints and assuming that it was made by a man—which is highly probable, of course—you arrive at a height of 5 feet, 3 inches. The smallest footprint, taken to be female and calculated with the upper end of the female ratio (to make her as tall as possible) results in a woman 4 feet, 4 inches tall, but actually the print was probably made by a child. For comparison: if you take a 6-foot man who wears a size 10 shoe (which means that his foot is a foot long) and scale him down to a height of 4 feet, his footprint would measure 20.3 centimeters, or just about 8 inches. The Aldène prints point to a small race, where apparently only a few individuals "towered" over 5 feet—presumably the same race (or at least the same size) as the sculptors of Tuc d'Audoubert.

This discovery makes for a rather varying-sized humanity in Europe after the last glaciation. The big 6-foot, 2-inch "Neanderthalians"[3] of the Mauer-Heidelberg type were

[3] This term was invented by the late Dr. Franz Weidenreich of the American Museum of Natural History. He suggested just three subdivisions of human beings: (A) the early human, *Homo erectus,* comprising *Pithecanthropus* and *Sinanthropus* (Peking Man); (B) *Homo neanderthalensis,* the "Neanderthalians," comprising a wide variety of primitive groups above *Homo erectus* but not yet *Homo sapiens;* and (C) *Homo sapiens,* Crô-Magnon and all living forms.

probably no longer around, but the equally tall Crô-Magnon were. The short Neanderthalians had probably just disappeared, but the still smaller modern Aldène type seems to have flourished. And elsewhere in Europe there was a type intermediate in size, the men running about 5 feet, 7 inches, the women about 5 feet, 3 inches. Except for possible remnants of short Neanderthalers these were all modern types; but now we know that the same variation in size, even more pronounced, prevailed in South Africa at an earlier stage.

The story of the discoveries of early men and of somehow related prehuman or near-human forms in South Africa will be told one day by somebody in a massive work. A good deal has been written already, but it must, of necessity, be incomplete because the sites are not yet exhausted and impressive new discoveries may take place any day.

The locality of the first finds was the district of Taungs, some 80 miles north of the Kimberly diamond fields. There, in the valley of the Harts River in Taungs, the Reverend Mr. Neville Jones had collected implements indicating human habitation for the last 500,000 years. They began with primitive stone weapons of the Early Stone Age, went on through more finished types right down to the coming of the Bushmen (in what would be very early historical times if the location were Egypt and not South Africa), and on from then to the hammer and spade of the Reverend Mr. Jones himself. In 1924 Professor Raymond A. Dart discovered most of the skull of something very much ape but also human. Unfortunately it was the skull of a child, corresponding in development to a human six-year-old. Professor Dart called it *Australopithecus*, which translates as "southern ape" (*austral* means south) but is apt to make the layman think of Australia ("Southland"), which never had any monkeys or apes. Other scientists felt inclined to talk about "Dart's child," partly because it was a child, partly because Dart behaved very much like a proud father. He said that this was the most important find since *Pithecanthropus*. By now everybody knows that he was right, but at first only two important experts, Dr. Robert Broom of the Transvaal Museum in Pretoria and Dr. William King Gregory of the American Museum of Natural History, believed him.

Nothing else happened for a long time, but the inhabitants of Transvaal were convinced that there had to be important things in their ground. It is a matter of record in serious scientific journals that soon after the First World War a Mr. Cooper, who owns a number of caves near Sterkfontein, wrote a little guidebook containing the sentence: "Come to Sterkfontein and find the Missing Link."

Dr. Robert Broom did just that, although one may say that it was not a missing "link" which was finally uncovered, but a missing chain. First he obtained the major portions of a skull, a fine mixture of ape and man characteristics, from those caves. Originally he thought it closely allied to Dart's *Australopithecus africanus* and called it *Australopithecus transvaalensis*. Then he reconsidered—they were not that closely related—and substituted the name *Plesianthropus* or Near-Man. That was in 1936. We now have all the bones of *Plesianthropus,* but they come from many individuals; so far no single complete or near-complete skeleton has turned up. In 1938 a schoolboy picked up some fossils at Kromdrai, about two miles away, which came into Broom's hand and proved to be remains of still another early type. It was named *Paranthropus* ("manlike") *robustus.*

A number of years later at a site at Swartkrans, three-quarters of a mile west of Sterkfontein, a jaw fragment of a truly gigantic type came to light, and a few years later skull fragments of still another type, which has been named *Telanthropus capensis.* As has been said, the complete story of these finds cannot be written yet, and it would therefore be useless to go into detail. But they all have been dated in the Pliocene, the most recent of the five subdivisions of the Tertiary Period. It is hard to say just what this means in years: if we consider the very end of the Pliocene it would be slightly less than a million, but the Pliocene itself lasted 6 million years and the fossils might well fit anywhere into its latter half. As regards the fossils themselves, present opinion seems to be that Paranthropus and Plesianthropus and the giant "Swartkrans Man" were divergent forms, not in the direct line of human evolution. But as for Telanthropus, Dr. J. T. Robinson of the Transvaal Museum in Pretoria has gone on record in calling him "a very primitive euhominid"—the last word meaning "true man."

But let's return to Australopithecus, who is of special interest to us here because of his small size. Among the variegated near-human forms inhabiting South Africa at that long-ago though somewhat uncertain date he was the pygmy. The most important finds were made by Dr. Dart some distance from the place where Plesianthropus and Telanthropus were uncovered. The Sterkfontein of Plesianthropus and the Swartkrans of Telanthropus lie not far from Krugersdorp, about 30 miles southwest of Pretoria. Dart's site of Australopithecus lies 125 miles from Pretoria in a northwesterly direction. Its name is Makapaansgat and the nearest town is Potgietersrust. Both these places are named after people with an interlinked fate. Makapaan was a native chieftain who attacked a caravan of Boers. The Boers, led by Potgieter, drove Makapaan and his men into a cave, piled brushwood into the entrance, and set it afire. Makapaan and his men were killed, but so was Potgieter. When Professor Dart came to those caves near Potgietersrust he saw that the breccia forming the roof of one of the caves contained charred bones.

It was worth investigating.

It turned out to be very much worth investigating.

The entire deposit had been consolidated by a calcareous cement. It was that dream of an archaeologist, a so-called "sealed site." There was evidence of fires, repeated fires. There were bones of Australopithecus. There were skulls of an extinct species of baboon, *Parapapio,* from the Pliocene period. And these skulls had been smashed, but not from above as might happen in a cave because of falling rocks. The skulls were smashed on their left, as if from a right-handed blow with a weapon, which may have been a thigh bone of some kind. (Specimens just like them were also found later in the Sterkfontein-Krugersdorp area.) To Professor Dart the whole picture built up to that of an erect little creature, about 4 feet tall, weighing between 80 and 100 pounds, knowing fire and wielding weapons, usually right-handed, and having a brain volume of 650 cubic centimeters, which is equal to that of the largest gorilla, half that of the average Homo sapiens, and only about 125 cubic centimeters less than that of the much larger Pithecanthropus.

These carnivorous hunters were therefore familiar with the use of fire and bludgeons and apparently used crude long bones as implements in similar fashion to *Sinanthropus*. Some of the penetrating puncture wounds which are also found may have been caused by the dagger-like horns of antelopes, and it is noteworthy that up to the present ungulate heads retaining their horns intact have never been found in the dumps. . . . These intelligent, energetic, erect and delicately proportioned little people were as competent as any other primitive human group in cavern life made comfortable by the use of fire, in the employment of long bones as lethal weapons, in the cunning and courage of the chase and in internecine strife. They had conquered the most formidable beasts of the field; they were already in the toils of an ever-accelerating evolutionary process occasioned by their intellectual struggle with the forces of nature and with their fellows.[4]

One expert, Dr. Sollas, expressed his regret that this astonishing early creature received such a clumsy name as *Australopithecus prometheus;* he said that it should have been Homunculus. Renaming something in science is a difficult and tedious process—and justly so—and it did not take place in this case. If it had, it might have been wrong.

Quite recently, in 1954, Dr. Kenneth P. Oakley, anthro-

---

[4] From "The Makapaansgat Proto-Human *Australopithecus prometheus,*" by Raymond A. Dart, *American Journal of Physical Anthropology,* September 1948.

pologist of the British Museum in London, examined the Makapaansgat sites and took samples with him. His position is almost precisely opposite to that of Professor Dart. The blacking of the bones, he declared, may be due to manganese dioxide instead of fire. And the ash, he stated, is not the remains of a wood fire. He admitted that it might be burned bat guano, since the guano of insect-eating bats consists mainly of insect wings and is highly inflammable. He even admits that a fire user who lives in caves might use bat guano at hand rather than carry wood over some distance and across possibly difficult terrain. But he does not think so:

> The doubtful evidence of fire in the *Australopithecus* layer at Makapaan is still *sub judice,* and even if confirmed could most readily be accounted for by a natural grass fire outside having ignited inflammable bat guano at the entrance to the cave—there are in fact records of comparable fires having occurred in recent times. (Kenneth P. Oakley, in *American Journal of Physical Anthropology,* 1954, 12,9.)

In short, we can't tell yet. We need more finds and we need more reliable dating. With the dating we have now it looks as if quite a number of clearly distinct species of sub- or pro- or para-humans lived simultaneously in the same area. Maybe they did—until finally the true humans won out.

It has even been suggested that one of these forms—interestingly and significantly again a pygmy form—is still alive in Africa. I have already told the little that is known in my book *The Lungfish, the Dodo, and the Unicorn*[5] but for the sake of completeness I'll repeat it here. The idea is based upon a rumor of something the natives are said to call *agogwe.* The British writer Frank W. Lane, after an extensive correspondence with British colonial officials, finally succeeded in finding two men who were willing to go on record with their observations. The following is quoted from Lane's *Nature Parade* (revised edition, London, 1944):

[5] New York: The Viking Press, 1948.

The first account, written by Captain W. Hichens, runs:

"Some years ago I was sent on an official lion hunt to this area (Ussure and Simbiti forests on the western side of the Wembare plains) and, while waiting in a forest glade for a man-eater, I saw two small, brown, furry creatures come from the dense forest on one side of the glade and disappear into the thickets on the other. They were like little men, about four feet high, walking upright, but clad in russet hair. The native hunter with me gaped in mingled fear and amazement. They were, he said, *agogwe*, the little furry men whom one does not see once in a lifetime. I made desperate efforts to find them, but without avail in that wellnigh impenetrable forest. They may have been monkeys, but, if so, they were no ordinary monkeys, nor baboons, nor colobus, nor Sykes, nor any other kind found in Tanganyika."

The other account was written by a Mr. Cuthbert Burgoyne:

"In 1927 I was with my wife coasting Portuguese East Africa in a Japanese cargo boat. We were sufficiently near land to see objects clearly with a glass of twelve magnifications. There was a sloping beach with light bush above, upon which several dozen baboons were hunting for and picking up shellfish or crabs, to judge by their movements. Two pure white baboons were among them. These are very rare, but I had heard of them previously. As we watched, two little brown men walked together out of the bush and down amongst the baboons. They were certainly not any known monkey and yet they must have been akin or they would have disturbed the baboons. They were too far away to see in detail, but these small human-like animals were probably between four and five feet tall, quite upright and graceful in figure. . . ."

After what Dart has said about his Australopithecus, these *agogwe* suddenly look very familiar. And since two reputable men have gone on record as having seen them, we'll have to accept the fact that there is something living in East Africa that looks from a distance like a furred small man. Judging from the experience with the other pygmies, we can hope that we'll find out one day what it is.

But Captain Foxe's "corpes" are likely to remain a riddle forever.

3: Natura Artis Magistra

THE difference between man and animal, one of my teachers was fond of explaining, preferably in front of one of the monkey habitats in the Berlin zoo, is not physical but mental, and hinges on a single concept. Imagine that somewhere in the African highlands, where the nights grow cold, a party of explorers have left their fire. It is still going and its warmth attracts a herd of freezing monkeys. They'll sit around and warm their hands and faces and bodies. They might even turn around once in a while to warm their back sides. But as the fire dies down and the warmth dwindles, there is nothing they know to do about it. A human being, even the most primitive bushman, would add fuel to the fire and keep it going. How did he, or his father's father, find out? He watched how a fire would creep up on a dead branch which happened to be near and drew the conclusion that he could help Nature along, even though he might not be able to put such a conclusion into words. But he would have grasped the principle: *natura artis magistra*, "Nature, art's instructor." To watch what can happen in nature and cause it to happen when and where you want it; that is what makes Man, and not accidental things like hair on the back or protruding canines.

Personally I would very much like to have this particular scene staged to see what would happen in reality. I must admit that my expectations tend to run to extremes; either the smell of the fire would frighten the monkeys so much that they would flee rather than be lured, or else, if they did come and warm themselves, they might realize that what makes the lovely warmth is wood, in which case the story of the sorcerer's apprentice might be re-enacted with fire.

But the general idea of the little lecture which culminated with *natura artis magistra* is the same that Benjamin Franklin expressed in the single sentence, "Man is a tool-bearing animal." Benjamin Franklin's statement, in turn, was later illustrated by something explorers in South America had actually observed.

South America is the home of a strange animal, the giant ant-eater. Just because of the strangeness of its appearance—an elongated tiny head at one end and an enormous hair plume of a tail at the other, and strangely turned-in feet with enormous claws—the giant ant-eater has become well-known, as a kind of natural abstract design that is intriguing to sculptors. Zoological gardens usually feel obliged to have a sign at the cage stating that the giant ant-eater does not eat ants and that the result would be fatal if it did. Its food in that cage usually consists of a mess of chopped hard-boiled eggs and raw hamburger (with vitamins added). In its natural habitat it eats termites. When hungry it will find a termite hill. Its fur, which is dense enough to stop bird shot, protects it well against any retaliation the termites are able to make. Using the powerful claws of the front feet, the ant-eater chops a hole into the hill. Regiments of termites boil out of the hole to defend their fortress; the ant-eater dangles its long, wormlike, and very sticky tongue among them, and the meal begins.

Some of the South American Indians eat termites too. To get them they arm themselves with a handy stone and a few long straws. The stone is used to batter a hole in the termite hill, and a straw is inserted into the hole. The defending termites attack the straw and bite into it with their mandibles, hanging on no matter what happens. What does happen is that the Indian puts the straw into his mouth and drags it out through clenched front teeth, leaving the termites inside to be ground up between teeth that are bigger than they are. Ethnologists are not certain whether the Indians invented this method on their own or whether they watched ant-eaters at work; the latter would be a slightly different case of *natura artis magistra*. But even if it is—or rather, especially if it is—it illustrates the case in point. The ant-eater cannot discard its large and (while walking) cumbersome claws when they have done their job, but the Indian can throw the stone away. The ant-eater's long tongue is fine for this purpose but also enforces a monotonous diet; the straws can be, and are, discarded. Specialized organ there, tool here, seems to express the difference between animal and man.

If this were the whole story the chapter would end right here. But it has been reliably reported that chimpanzees moisten straws with their saliva and place them in the path of ants, then drag the straw through their teeth, just like the South American Indians. If one insists that they must have learned it from another animal, the African aardvark might have been the unwitting instructor, but it is more likely that they thought it up themselves. But whether they "learned it by watching an aardvark"—not that I believe this theory even for a moment—or "invented" it themselves, we have here the undeniable fact that an animal has done what is supposed to be the prerogative of Man. It has used a "tool," something that was not a part of its body and which could be (and was) discarded afterward. But if one animal can invent a tool for a specific purpose for which its own organs are inadequate, there is no reason to deny categorically that another animal may invent a tool too.

Over this discussion, one might say in dim outline, hovers the word "eolith." If these eoliths, as their discoverers maintained, are very simple and very primitive tools, do we also have to conclude that they were made by very primitive men?

Or could they, conceivably, be the products of some animal? Are there animals which use tools, not only occasionally, like the chimpanzees with a taste for formic acid, but habitually?

Before I try to furnish some answer to this question, I would like to relate a discovery made during the winter of 1954-55, which shows just how important specific knowledge may be for the proper interpretation of evidence. The discovery was made in those fabulous limestone caves of Australopithecus at Makapaansgat in Central Transvaal. A number of ancient stone tools, of the kind called "fist-axes," were found there. According to Professor Raymond Dart they represent "the oldest and most primitive stone culture in South Africa." If these fist-axes were a little more primitive than they are, and if they, like some of the eoliths, were tiny in size, the question would have been inevitable whether the find was some of the tools of Australopithecus, definite stone tools made by something that was definitely not "human." In this particular case the problem happens not to exist. These fist-axes were made by true men who have been given the name of Kafuans; a name coined after the pattern of Neanderthalians, because their former existence was first established in the area of the Kafu River near Lake Albert. The South African experts think that when the Kafuans moved into the Makapaansgat valley, equipped with fist-axes and presumably with enough reasoning to feed dead wood to a dying fire, Australopithecus was probably still living there. If so, Australopithecus probably moved out because the Kafuans moved in.

But now: do animals use tools?

Since our definition of a tool is that it is "extra-organic" (does not belong to the body) and can therefore be discarded or abandoned, we first come into a kind of twilight zone where the definition itself must be amended. A bird's nest built of twigs, or dry grass, or even mud is clearly extra-organic, but it frequently has a feather lining. The feathers

often belong to the bird that built the nest, but they have
been detached for the purpose and can later be abandoned.
Incidentally, a bird's nest is by no means its "home"; it is a
nursery exclusively and is abandoned by parents and children
alike once it has served this purpose.

Two other examples of animal structures that come to
mind immediately once the cue "building" has been uttered
are the spider's web and the bee's honeycomb. In both cases
the substance is an excretion of the body itself, but once
excreted the materials lose their "organic" character. You
can tear the spider's web or steal the bee's honeycomb without harming the creatures themselves; in fact, either would
be abandoned anyway after a certain length of time. That
even much higher animals may still use body excretions for
building is shown by the nest of the salangane or "edible
swift." This bird builds its nests exclusively of a kind of
saliva which hardens as soon as it comes into contact with
the air. The nests look somewhat like shallow saucers of
white porcelain—or like certain sea shells—and are used to
make a very interesting soup, although they must be harvested before the mother bird put them to their intended use.

One of the most fantastic examples of the use of a substance produced by the body is found on Java. There the
trees are inhabited by rather large frogs. Their scientific
name is *Polypedates reinwardtii,* but they are better known
as the flying frogs of Java. The latter name is partly correct—
the frogs cannot really fly, but their feet are large enough so
that the membranes between the long toes act as a parachute
when the frog, jumping after an insect, misses his landing
space. The frog's skin needs moisture to function properly,
but apparently the leaves of the trees of the Javanese forest
are wet enough; in any event the frog never descends to the
water. Other frogs and toads—remember the midwife toad
in Chapter 1—also stay away from bodies of water and manage
with wet grass and moist soil, but for propagation most of
them have to return to the pond. The flying frog has over-

come that problem too, although its tadpoles need liquid
water for a while.

When mating, the male sits on the back of the female,
holding on with his forelegs. The female's forelegs hold on
to a tree branch, high above the forest floor. The eggs, when
they begin to appear, are imbedded in a thick gelatinous
mass, as are the eggs of almost all frogs. But as soon as the
eggs begin to appear the hind legs of both parents go to
work, kicking and beating the jelly into something resembling whipped cream. When the work has been done the
parents extricate themselves, and the result of their combined "labor" is a handful of foam hanging from a branch.
On the outside, where the foam is in contact with the air, it
hardens quickly and forms a rubbery shell. On the inside the
foam gradually ceases to be foam and turns into water so
that the little tadpoles can go through the aquatic phase of
their life in relative safety.

In addition to the use of body excretions as construction
material, and even further from the utilization of truly extra-
organic matter, there are a few cases of animals "growing a
tool."

One example is furnished by an animal of the high seas
which is related to the octopus and the squid. In past periods
of our earth's history most octopus-like animals grew protective shells, many of them quite pretty and some of truly
extraordinary dimensions: one such fossil octopus shell,
found near a place called Seppenrade in western Germany
and named *Pachydiscus seppenradensis,* measures close to
$8\frac{1}{2}$ feet across. In the present only the nautilus, which is
not even very closely related to the earlier form, still grows a
shell, and its shell is as much a part of its body as is the shell
of a garden snail; the animal, forcibly removed, does not
survive. But another relative of the octopus, the paper
nautilus *(Argonauta argo),* grows a detachable shell. More
precisely, the female paper nautilus does; the male doesn't.
The shell, white and fragile and, from the human point of

view, far prettier than that of the true nautilus, seems to be used mainly as a cradle for the young. Then, like a bird's nest, it is abandoned.

The second example of a "grown tool" is also marine. The animal in question is tiny, less than half an inch in length, and is a member of a group which to scientists looks as if it represented an unsuccessful attempt at becoming vertebrates.

The name of the particular marine creature is *Oikopleura,* which is derived from *oikos,* the Greek word for "house," or, alternately, from *oiketēs,* which means the inhabitant of a house. Special cells in Oikopleura's skin—they are called oikoplasts—produce a substance which is chemically related to cellulose. So far this sounds as if Oikopleura grew itself a kind of armor, just as a crab does. And even the additional information that this substance is transparent does not yet seem too strange. Tiny crabs of the high seas also have nearly transparent armor. The interesting point is that the "house" built by Oikopleura is more like a house than a suit of armor. It is not close-fitting at all—one can probably best describe it by saying that Oikopleura grows a barrel around itself. Oikopleura's method of locomotion is exceedingly modern; it propels itself by the reaction of a water jet. The locomotion itself provides the food, more or less as if birds sucked into the air intake of a jet plane were somehow passed on to the pilot as lunch. The microscopic sea life which is sucked in in front is utilized; the water is jetted out to the rear. Obviously, indigestible particles will remain in the space between the animal proper and its comparatively large "barrel," or tunic, as it is called in scientific language. After some time enough refuse will have accumulated in the tunic to make things uncomfortable for Oikopleura. Then it simply slips out of the tunic and grows a new one. And if a large enemy, a fish, snaps at the tunic, the animal usually escapes.

But while Oikopleura is probably the only creature that

can *grow* detachable and jettisonable armor, the principle
of such armor is not at all rare in the seas. Everybody knows
of the hermit crab, which hides its soft and unarmored tail
safely away in the empty shell of a marine snail. To add
some armament which is not completely passive the crab
then puts a sea anemone or two—mostly of the variety *Sagar-
tia parasitica*—on top of the shell. The sea anemones can
sting, which is a protection for the crab. On their part they
acquire a mobility normally denied to their kind, thereby
increasing their chance of catching prey. The crab even
feeds them directly, so that everybody is happy with the
results of the alliance. But this leads us away from the use of
extra-organic tools into the vast realm of symbiosis. Besides,
the snail shell, though a tool for the crab, is something that
the crab finds ready-made, though it may have to eat the
maker first. An animal that builds its armor is more
interesting.

The prime example of this activity also lives in the water,
but it is in fresh water that *Macronema,* the caddis worm,
makes individual armor which, by virtue of the fact that
it does so under water, is even portable. Like many
popular names, the name "caddis worm" is zoologically
wrong. It is not a worm but an insect of the order of the
Trichoptera, a still existing line of fairly ancient insects
which in the past gave rise to the far more spectacular tribe
of the butterflies. The winged adult insects neither look very
impressive nor do anything interesting; it is the larva that
deserves attention. The larvae begin by spinning what might
be a cocoon when finished, but it always stays open at one
end. At one stage it looks very much like the cut-off finger
of a filmy glove. The insect sits inside, with head and several
pairs of legs sticking out. Then the glove finger is reinforced
with extra-organic material: with tiny pebbles or with the
empty shells of young freshwater snails, or with thin dead
stalks of underwater plants, all carefully cut to equal length
and fitted together to form a hexagonal tube.

The choice of reinforcing material is apparently governed by environment, or may even be determined by whatever was picked up first accidentally, but once a caddis "worm"

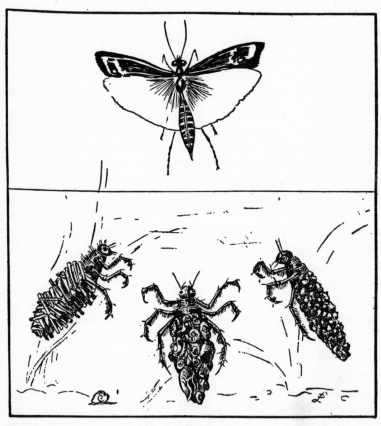

Larvae of the caddis "worm," with different types of self-manufactured armor. *Top,* the finished insect, a survivor of the type which gave rise to the butterflies

has started with a material it sticks to it. If small shells form the armor it consists of small shells exclusively—or of pebbles, or of sticks. No "artistic arrangements" with sticks on top and bottom, pebbles on the sides, and a round snail shell for the tail end.

But whether we are discussing birds' nests of twigs or of mud, or caddis-worm cases, or the dams built by beavers, the nests built by rodents, the mud puddles constructed by some South American frogs to assure a water basin for their tadpoles, the pebble dams built under water by a number of freshwater fishes to prevent the current from sweeping their eggs away, the principle is always the same. The material used is properly extra-organic, often even inorganic (though that doesn't really make a difference), but the activities are all performed by the organs, whether bills, mandibles, teeth, or feet—not really what one would call "tools."

But some animals, a fair number of them in fact, do use tools.

My first example is again an insect; to be systematic about it, an insect of the order of the *Hymenoptera,* suborder *Apocrita,* genus *Sphex.* It is a kind of wasp—in fact *"sphex"* is just the Greek word for "wasp"—which in entomological English is pin-pointed a little more precisely as one of the "thread-waisted wasps," which I find hardly easier to pronounce than *sphex.* The thread-waisted wasps of the genus *Sphex* all have one procedure in common: they dig narrow, nearly vertical tunnels in sandy soil, between 1¾ and 2 inches in depth. In this tunnel they place one or several insects that have been skillfully paralyzed by a sting into just the right nerve center, and one egg. In time the egg hatches and lives on the provisions left by the mother wasp. The larva, without leaving the tunnel, grows to its full size and then pupates *in situ,* emerging as a completely developed wasp. But if the mother left the tunnel open, other insects or even birds would find it promptly, so before leaving the wasp carries sand to the hole and pushes enough in to fill it to the top, every once in a while tamping the sand with its head. But some members of the genus *Sphex* do not use their heads directly for this purpose. Instead, they take a small

One of the thread-waisted wasps pounding sand into a hole with the
aid of a small pebble, probably the only example of a true tool
among insects

pebble in their mandibles and pound the loose sand in until
it is as firm as the undisturbed soil around the tunnel.

Another true use of a tool by an insect is the "weaving" of
nests by the emerald ants of Java, India, and Ceylon. Their
scientific name is *Oecophylla smaragdina;* the word *oecophylla,* meaning "leaf house," was chosen originally as a
descriptive term. But it is not quite descriptive enough, for
a "leaf house" could easily be on the ground, built of dead
leaves or of leaves cut for the purpose. The leaf house of the
Oecophylla ants is high up in the trees and the leaves are the
living leaves of the tree which are woven together by silky
threads. It was just this last fact which was puzzling, since
the Oecophylla ants were never seen to spin a thread when
observed on the ground. Nor did the dissection of Oecophylla
ants under the microscope reveal anything even remotely
resembling the spinning equipment of, say, a spider. It was
less than half a century ago that a traveling zoologist, Franz
Doflein, observed what actually took place up there in the
boughs.

Worker ants, working in regular gangs, held the leaves

together, clinging to the edge of one with all six legs and holding the edge of the other leaf with their mandibles. If the distance between the two leaves was too great, an ant would climb out to the edge and would be held by the man-

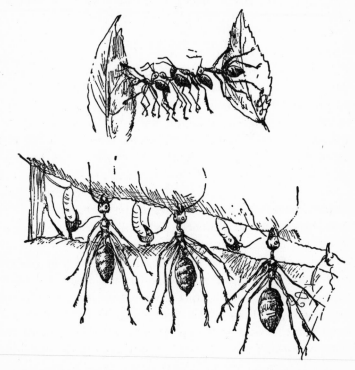

Workers of the tree-dwelling ant *Oecophylla smaragdina* repairing a leaf nest by utilizing the spinning ability of their own larvae

dibles of another ant. Then a third would climb out to be held by the mandibles of the ant farthest out, and so on. They produced chains of seven or eight ants to reach the edge of the other leaf. Once this had been accomplished the whole chain would slowly retreat to the leaf on which the supporting ant was standing, until the leaves had been pulled together sufficiently so that they could be held in place by a single row of ants. Then another gang of workers would appear, each one carrying an ant larva in its mandibles. Franz Doflein then saw that, while the adult ant could not spin a thread, the larva could. Using their own larvae like upholstery needles—or like shuttles, to use Doflein's term—the ants would then weave, or sew, the leaves together.

The larva of still another insect—*Myrmeleon formicalynx,* the ant lion, this time of the order of *Neuroptera*—is the inventor of artillery. As is the case with the caddis "worm," the adult insect, the imago, is not interesting, in either looks or actions. The larva digs a cone-shaped pit in dry sand and hides at, or rather under, the bottom, completely covered with sand. When an ant passes the rim of the pit the ant lion throws grains of sand with unerring accuracy, so that the ant loses its footing and slides down the side of the conical pit and into the waiting mandibles at the bottom.

One other animal "shoots" extra-organic matter (there are several—insects, reptiles, and mammals—which squirt body fluids of one kind or another) to obtain its food. This is *Toxotes jaculator,* the Siamese archer fish, first brought to the attention of science in a communication read to the Royal Society of London on March 15, 1764 (*Transactions,* vol. LV for the year 1764, pp. 89-91). The member of the Society who had sent the communication was one John Albert Schlosser, a doctor in Amsterdam, but the information had come from the governor of a hospital in Batavia, Hommel by name.

When it [the fish] spies a fly sitting on the plants that grow in shallow water, it swims on to the distance of four, five or six feet, and then, with surprising dexterity, it ejects out of its tubular mouth a single drop of water, which never fails striking the fly into the sea, where it soon becomes its prey. . . .

Unfortunately the specimen which was sent along with the report was *not* a specimen of *Toxotes jaculator,* and although the error was corrected as soon as possible it cast some doubt on the whole story. More than a hundred years later two leading experts on the fishes of this region, Dr. Pieter Bleeker and Dr. Francis Day, denied independently but vehemently that the fish ever performed in this manner or was even capable of so performing. Dr. Bleeker, who was the more gentle of the two—at least when it came to written words—declared that there had probably been an error of observation. There had been, but in another sense than Dr. Bleeker assumed. Hugh M. Smith, who was fisheries adviser to the Kingdom of Siam earlier in this century, had pointed out that the Malays use the same name for the archer fish Toxotes and a coral-reef fish, *Chelmo rostratus*. This, in all probability, is also the reason that the wrong fish was sent to London with Hommel's report; it was a specimen of Chelmo too!

That the archer fish actually shoots water droplets has been definitely known and generally accepted only since 1902, when the Russian ichthyologist Nikolai F. Zolotnitsky reported on an extensive series of observations and experiments with captive specimens. The shooting mechanism is formed by a double ridge on the roof of the fish's mouth which becomes a tube when the tongue is placed against it.

With the tongue closely pressed against the palate, the sudden compression of the gill covers forces water from the pharynx into the palatine canal; and with the tip of the tongue acting as a valve, the flow of water under pressure is regulated. It is the obvious habit of the fish to coordinate the compression of the gill covers with the momentary lifting of the tongue from the front end of the tube, permitting the escape of a single drop of water. With the jaws partly separated and the mouth reaching or projecting slightly about the surface the drop of water is ejected for a distance that depends on the pressure. It is easy to understand how, with the pharyngeal cavity acting as both a reservoir for water ammunition and a compression chamber, it is possible for the fish to shoot drops of water in quick succession, as has been frequently observed, or the water may be expelled in the form of a jet when the valve is kept open longer.[1]

Toxotes rarely misses. It can shoot insects on the wing, though normally the targets are insects sitting on plants which the fish stalks carefully and successfully. That the impact is sufficient to knock down any insect is proved by an observation by Hugh M. Smith, who saw a Toxotes shoot a small lizard which fell into the water. Presumably the lizard escaped, however, for the mouth of Toxotes is quite small and it has no weapons other than its "blowpipe." Incidentally, one should not smoke in the dark near waters where the archer fish lives or is kept. To the fish the glow of a cigarette indicates a firefly or glowworm of some kind, and it extinguishes the cigarette with great skill.

Except for stone-throwing monkeys, no other animal uses missiles, but one bird has invented bombing. When the well-known British ornithologist John Gould was studying the birds of Australia over a century ago it was reported to him that a large hawk of the inland areas, the black-breasted buzzard, was fond of the big eggs of the emu. To obtain them it would frighten a brooding emu off the eggs with sudden dives and a wild flapping of wings, then take a stone up and drop it on the eggs. Inserting a claw into the hole in an egg broken by the falling stone, it would carry it off to its nest. Gould did not see this himself but the story was substantiated to a large extent by Australian bird watchers who were surprised to find the shells of emu eggs in buzzard nests.[2]

[1] *The Fresh-Water Fishes of Siam, or Thailand* by Hugh M. Smith (U. S. National Museum *Bulletin* No. 188), pp. 494-95.

[2] The behavior of some other birds is such that the report appears credible. The large eagle of the southern Balkans carries the so-called Greek tortoise up and drops it on the rocks to break its armor; there is a story that a Greek monk was accidentally killed that way. And it is an established fact that seagulls have damaged cars on New Jersey highways by dropping clams on them, the purpose of the performance being of course to crack the hard shell of the clam.

When the interior of Australia was first explored, travelers often came across quaint little structures that had obviously been built by somebody or something. Usually located among low shrubs, they consisted of a platform of small sticks, laid side by side. On two opposite sides of the platform other sticks, a foot and a half or so in length, were stuck upright into the ground, making two walls. If the sticks curved they were always placed so that they curved over the platform, occasionally forming a small tunnel. And at one end of the platform there was an accumulation of objects, hundreds of them, covering an area larger by far than the platform. There were snail shells, empty cicada shells, flowers, white and yellow pebbles, lots of small bones, bird feathers, and pieces of cast-off snake skins.

The builder of these structures was never in sight—or so it seemed—and the whole was as mysterious as possible. A Captain Stokes who traveled in inner Australia during the years 1837-43 came to the conclusion that native women had built them to amuse their children. Sir George Grey, Colonial Governor at the time, preferred to think that kangaroos made them, apparently on the theory that such a queer creature as the kangaroo was capable of anything.

Today virtually everybody knows that these are the "playgrounds," or "arbors," or "bowers" of the bower birds. The birds built them in addition to their true nests, which are simple shallow basket nests up in the trees. Australian experts are debating among themselves on whether the ground structures should be referred to as "courtship bowers," or as "playgrounds" with only incidental relationship to courtship. Whatever the primary, secondary, or incidental purpose, the important thing is that the birds built them, and that at least one, the satin bower bird, uses a tool in doing so. The tool is not used for the building itself, which is done with the beak, but in a finishing operation, which is painting.

That the birds actually indulge in this practice was defi-

nitely established by observations in the National Park of
New South Wales around 1930. An Australian ornithologist,
Alec H. Chisholm,[3] wrote as follows:

Many times I had seen bowers containing blackened sticks
and had imagined these to have been charred in fires. That hasty
conclusion was dispelled a few years ago. It was established then
that the bird actually brings charcoal to the bower, munches it
into a paste, and, holding his head sideways, paints each stick
of the inside walls with his beak! Moreover, he carries fragments
of soft bark to the bower and holds one of these in the beak
while applying the mixture. We surmised at first that these
scraps of bark were used as brushes; but it now seems more
probable that they are by way of being stoppers, or corks, to
prevent the mixture oozing from the tip of the beak while it is
being applied to the walls with the sides of the beak.

After quoting an eye-witness account of the painting operation, Mr. Chisholm slightly modified his statement about
the function of the piece of bark by writing:

Thus, as I say, the scrap of bark is a "cork" rather than a
"brush," but it would not be surprising to discover that it served
both purposes. The difficulty in deciding this point lies in the
fact that the wad is not visible while the painting is in progress.

Apparently birds, because they habitually carry things
around in their beaks, have repeatedly found that something
held in the beak will make a tool. One large parrot-like bird
of New Guinea is known to feed almost exclusively on very
hard and very smooth palm nuts. Occasionally it carries
them around, with the nut wrapped in a coarse leaf so that
it cannot slip away. Some small insect-eating Australian birds
use a dry stalk of grass to pry for insects under loose bark
where their short bills do not reach. The finches of the
Galápagos Islands—almost, though not quite, at the antipodal
point from their Australian colleagues—do the same.

[3] In his book *Bird Wonders of Australia*. Sydney: Angus and Robertson Ltd.,
1935.

The bowers of the bower birds were not the only bird structures in Australia which were mistaken for something else by early explorers and settlers. Visiting scientists were occasionally told by settlers that there were "native burial mounds" in the scrub in this or that direction. There were mounds all right, and of considerable size too—one was 15 feet high and measured some 60 feet in circumference—but they were not made by the natives and had not served for burials. They were the product of the mound-building birds of Australia, of which there are three kinds: the talegallus (the Australians call it scrub turkey), the megapodes, and the mallee-fowl. Mound building begins at the end of the Australian winter (say late in August), and when the mound is large enough the birds place their eggs in the mass of decaying vegetation. The eggs are arranged in a circle, a few inches apart, and are placed so that they rest in a vertical position, with the more pointed end downward. The distance from the eggs to the top of the mound varies; in some cases it is just 2 feet, in others as much as 5 feet. Far from being burial mounds, the heaps of soil and leaves are incubators, kept at a useful temperature by the chemical heat generated by decaying plant matter.[4]

The oldest egg incubator built by human beings is rather old by human standards, since it was made in ancient Egypt, but the Australian version is certainly much older. It is old enough to have caused profound changes in the birds as

[4] Several Australian scientists hold that this is true only of the mounds of talegallus and megapode, and that the mounds of the mallee-fowl are built in dry areas where vegetable matter would not decay and that they must be heated by the sun directly. It is an interesting fact that relatives of this bird which live on Celebes do bury their eggs in the black volcanic sand near the shore, which is heated by the tropical sun to such a degree that the eggs, if left at the surface, would be cooked instead of hatched. Those birds living in the interior of Celebes were once believed to migrate to the black sands of the shore at egg-laying time but were later found to utilize volcanic heat instead of solar heat; they bury their eggs near hot springs. The discoverers of this fact, two cousins named Sarasin, admitted that the first conclusion they drew from their discovery was personal rather than scientific—the finding of a hot spring meant a welcome addition to their food supply.

well as in the eggs. The birds no longer practice "normal" brooding at all. And the eggs have shells so fragile that they cannot be hatched by domestic chickens; hens will invariably break them. But people have succeeded in hatching such eggs by imitating the bird's mound.

With so many interesting and intriguing instances of the use of tools among birds one should expect to find more and even better examples among the far more intelligent mammals. But apparently the organization of the mammalian body is such that there is simply no need or not even any room for the use of tools to satisfy its requirements. Ingenious "tricks" there are many, but I know of only one mammal below the monkeys that uses a tool. That is the sea otter, which has its separate chapter in this book (Chapter 11).

When it comes to monkeys and apes the field seems at first glance to be unlimited. The books are full of stories of monkeys who learned to use a key to open the cupboard where their food was kept, who washed their own garments and spread them out to dry. There are innumerable stories about chimpanzees who learned to smoke with relish, who became expert bicycle riders, who ate their meals sitting at table with their keepers—anything and almost everything, all the way up to a female chimpanzee who once lived in the Vienna zoo and on cold days, or on command, started a fire in an old-fashioned coal stove to heat her milk. All this, however, no matter how amusing it may be to watch or to read about, has absolutely no bearing on the tool problem. If you can teach tricks to sea lions, to dogs, and to horses, why should you not be able to teach useful actions to a chimpanzee, which is obviously far more intelligent than a dog, and which, in addition, has a physical build that enables it to handle utensils designed for humans almost as easily as a human does?

The problem was not what an ape could learn when taught, or what it might imitate after watching people. The problem was to learn what it would invent on its own, without being shown. The comparatively small, usually cooperative, and intelligent chimpanzee was the natural choice over the more gloomy gorilla and the less well-known orangutan. For the purpose, newly caught chimpanzees which had had no chance to watch people in action would be needed, and they would have to be kept under conditions as nearly "natural" as possible and just be watched.

The idea of establishing such a station occurred in about 1909 to a physician, the neurologist Dr. Rothmann, in Berlin. He convinced the Prussian Academy of Sciences that the scientific gain would be well worth the expense, and after he had also obtained a few private donations the Observation Station for Anthropoid Apes was established. The locality chosen was the island of Tenerife in the Canary Islands. The main reason for the choice was the climate, which should be pleasing to the chimpanzees. A secondary reason was the nearness to the African continent, which would furnish the supply. Finally it turned out also to be a wise choice politically—since the islands belong to Spain, which was neutral in the First World War, the work was not hampered by the outbreak of the war. Professor Wolfgang Köhler became the scientific leader of the venture. The number of chimpanzees observed varied between seven and nine. None of them had ever been in a circus or a zoological garden; they were caught for the Observation Station and brought to Tenerife as fast as was then possible.

Not counting the houses where Professor Köhler, his staff members, and the keepers lived, the Observation Station consisted of not much more than a wire-net fence enclosing a large open area, and a few sheds for the animals to sleep in.

I don't know whether Toynbee had already evolved his theory of "challenge and response" at that time, but the work at the Observation Station proceeded as if these words had been painted on the gate as the fundamental guide. The challenge was compounded of the empty stomach of the chimpanzee and a few bananas in a difficult location. The response was what Professor Köhler wanted to see.

The first few experiments were simple. The bananas were placed in a small basket suspended from the ceiling; by means of a string the observer could make the basket move like a pendulum. Any child could have figured out that the bananas could be obtained if one climbed one wall to a certain height and reached for the basket at the right instant. Of course the experimenter had seen to it that this particular wall *could* be climbed easily. The question was whether the chimpanzees were able to think clearly enough to understand the situation. Three of them were brought in. One did not respond; maybe he happened not to be hungry at the moment. Another tried to jump for the basket. The third watched quietly for a short while, then suddenly turned to the wall, climbed up, and received the basket as it swung his way. It was clearly an act engendered by previous thought.

The next experiment consisted in placing the bananas outside the fence. The bananas were beyond the reach of the ape's arm, but a straw was tied to them and its end was within reach. That experiment was simply too easy. The chimpanzees, after a probing look, reached for the straw. In this case they obviously had "previous experience," pulling one twig of a tree branch in order to get another twig with ripe fruit into reach. Then the bananas were placed outside the fence without an attached straw, but there was a stick inside the fence. For about half an hour a chimpanzee tried unsuccessfully to stretch his arm long enough; then he saw the stick and used it, putting its end on the ground *beyond* the bananas at first try. Professor Köhler repeated this experiment with another chimpanzee who had been brought in only three days earlier. He first tried to reach the bananas directly, then sat down and complained, but after seven minutes he saw the stick and used it, somewhat clumsily but successfully.

In one case a chimpanzee taught the professor something that he had not expected. The bananas were high up under the ceiling but a pole was provided with which they could be beaten down. This was the normal "human" solution in the mind of the experimenter. Several chimpanzees did reason it out and acted accordingly. (It would be interesting to learn whether chimpanzees in the open beat fruit off a tree with a dead branch.) But one chimpanzee showed that there was another solution, the chimpanzee solution. He placed the pole vertically on the ground right under the bananas *and then climbed up before it had time to fall!*

Another experiment was made in a cage with walls too smooth for climbing. The bananas were nailed into the corner high up. All the chimpanzees were tried. They all tried to reach the fruit by jumping for a while and then gave up. Finally one, walking to and fro in the cage nervously, paused in front of a wooden box and after a moment pushed the box in the direction of the banana corner (some 10 feet away), jumped on the box, and jumped for the fruit from the top of the box. Again, the experiment was repeated with a chimpanzee who had just recently arrived and had had no opportunity to watch even the other chimpanzees. The new arrival—Koko was his name—at first jumped, then tried to beat the bananas down by using a loop of the long line with which he was tethered to the wall. After a pause he looked at the box, then at the bananas, and then pushed the box, or rather gave it a short push which failed to move it. Stepping back he looked again at the goal and at the box and gave it another tentative push. A third push moved the box (in the direction of the goal) by 3 or 4 inches. As if this had convinced him that the box could be moved, he suddenly pulled it to the corner and got his fruit. For very high-hanging fruit the chimpanzees combined methods, beating for the fruit with a pole from the top of a box. And one day a chimpanzee who could not reach high enough from the top of his box brought a second box and piled it on top of the first. Even three boxes were piled on top of one another, not in a manner one would call neat or even safe, but the superior

Chimpanzees at the Anthropoid Observation Station piling up boxes to reach their food.

speed of the ape made up for the lack of durability of the structure.

Things did not go quite as calmly as I am describing them. There were hours of sulking, long and loud complaints, occasional fits of rage, and every once in a while a chimpanzee would beat a box which could not be pushed easily or which turned out to be too small. The whole sequence of experiments proved as clearly as possible that the chimpanzees thought. If they had been guided by instinct, or even habit, the performance would have been different: it would have been much smoother and without any room for improvisations.

So far Köhler's chimpanzees had not done anything which other animals might not accomplish too; their tool use had been the same. It had been on the level of the "unimproved tool." The next higher step would be the "improved tool," the tool which has to be shaped in some manner to fulfill its function especially well. As an intermediate step one might imagine that an unimproved tool which happens to have an especially useful shape would be kept for re-use when required.

No instance of the latter was ever observed,[5] but two of Köhler's chimpanzees did try to improve their tools. The idea was to see whether they might try to lengthen a stick. One female called Eve was given a stick to reach for fruit outside the fence. The stick was too short, and Eve, after trying for a while, remembered that she had another stick in the cage, though it was shorter than the one she was using. She took the shorter stick, put the ends of both in her hand, reached carefully around, and, holding on to both, continued her efforts. Of course the attempt was a failure but the trend of thought—that "two sticks are longer than one"—was correct.

[5] One may make a case, though not a very strong one, for the British song thrush. The bird eats snails and beats the snail against a stone to crack the shell. It is known that the thrushes have their preferred stones, which are actually called "thrush anvils."

A male chimpanzee, called Sultan, was then supplied with two hollow reeds. The discrepancy between the distance to the fruit and the lengths of the reeds was such that Sultan could see at a glance that neither would reach. What he did was to push one reed all the way through the fence and then push it with the second reed until the first had reached the fruit. He succeeded in touching it indirectly and could move it a bit but naturally could not pull it back. About an hour later the keeper came to Professor Köhler and reported that Sultan, after the reeds had been thrown back into his cage, had played with them for a while until he noticed that the thinner reed fitted into the hole of the larger one. He pushed it in for a short distance and then at once turned to the fence to try for the bananas. Professor Köhler arrived just in time to see the reeds fall apart. But Sultan knew by then what could be done, he put the reeds together again and pulled the bananas carefully, a short distance at a time, in his direction. "The method seemed to please him very much, he looked very much alert, pulled all the fruits to the fence without taking the time to eat any of them. When I [Köhler] took his double reed apart he put it together again and began to pull completely unimportant objects to the fence." The following day Sultan progressed another step. The lengthened reed proved awkward on occasion because of its greater length, so Sultan would take it apart himself as soon as the extra length was no longer needed.

I'll use Köhler's own words, with only a few parenthetical remarks left out, to tell of Sultan's highest accomplishment:

In addition to a reed with a rather large opening [Sultan] had at his disposal a small wooden board which was just a bit too wide to fit the opening. Sultan took the board and tried to push it in . . . since this did not work he bit into the reed, breaking out a long splinter. As soon as he had the splinter he tried to fit it into the other undamaged end of the reed; a surprising development which would have solved the problem if the splinter had not happened to be a little too wide too. He then took the board again and began to bite into it, very logically on both sides of the same end to reduce its width. After he had chewed the (very hard) wood for a while he tried whether it would fit into the undamaged opening of the reed and continued to work—one has to use the term "work" here—until the board went into the opening for about 2 centimeters. But 2 centimeters were not

The chimpanzee Sultan trying to lengthen a stick

enough and the reed always fell off the board again. By then Sultan was apparently tired of biting wood, he preferred to shave off the splinter [with his teeth] and soon succeeded in wedging it firmly into the end of the reed.

Sultan, without any other aid than that rendered in making the materials available, did make an "improved tool." With regard to the eoliths, the reason for the whole discussion, this result proves that their makers did not necessarily have to be "human." All they needed was the ability to think to some extent and a "challenge" which forced them to do so.

I know of no more recent work along these lines—the Yerkes Laboratories of Primate Biology at Orange Park, Florida, where more than fifty chimpanzees are assembled, are devoted to entirely different purposes—but some accidental observations of *Natura artis magistra* (in its most literal sense) have been published.

In 1942 Dr. Julian S. Huxley was watching a young gorilla in his cage in the London Zoo. The cage was illuminated by a strong electric light which cast the gorilla's shadow on the white wall. "Seeing his shadow before him at one moment, he stopped, looked at it, and proceeded to trace its outline with its forefinger." The young ape repeated this twice more, then turned away to play. Although carefully watched, he was never seen to do it again. When Dr. Huxley's report was published, a Mr. J. Leonard Bowen wrote to him that he had seen something similar several years earlier: "Large numbers of large long-tailed monkeys romp about the little hill station of Matheran, near Bombay. I frequently saw such monkeys trace the outline of one of their hands in the dust, using a twig held almost as one would hold a pencil. Other monkeys inspected the traced outlines with a show of interest, walking round and round the spot with what seemed to be an anxious manner."

In other words, even a prehistoric tracing, if simple enough, could be of "subhuman" origin. It is obviously impossible to draw a sharp borderline, unless that old classroom story should hold true after all—if "it" fed a fire, "he" was human.

4: The Abominable Snowmen

SOMEWHERE in the high valleys to the north of India, next to and between the highest mountain peaks of our planet, there is something unknown, or, at the very least, something unexplained. What evidence there is consists mainly of footprints. They are, as is logical, considering the high altitudes, footprints in snow. For that reason they are not only rather impermanent evidence, but have the further inconvenience that under the action of the sun's rays they will change both shape and size.

The natives of the region claim that these footprints are made by beings frightful and inimical; beings unknown to the white visitors and therefore unnamed in the visitors' language. The white visitors would much prefer to think that the footprints were made by bears, which can be frightful and inimical if hungry enough. But this the natives energetically contradict. Not bears but "snowmen" left these footprints, and the visitors were very lucky that they came across the footprints only and missed encountering their originators.

The visitor to the Himalayas, after his return, is usually asked whether he heard anything about the snowmen and feels moved to write an article about either his or other people's experiences. The article, as a rule, begins more or less as follows: "The mystery originated very fittingly with the first Mount Everest expedition, the reconnaissance of 1921. . . ." This refers to the now famous report by the leader of that expedition, Colonel C. K. Howard-Bury, who, accompanied by five other white explorers and by twenty-six native porters, made an attempt at the north col of Mount Everest in September of that year. Using the Kharta glacier as the best means of approach the expedition headed for the Lhakpa La, a pass at a height of 22,000 feet. There, in soft snow, they saw the tracks of hares and of foxes and also, to their intense surprise, a track which could well have been made by a barefoot man.

The porters, Colonel Howard-Bury reported, at once said that these were the tracks of a *metohkangmi*.[1] He also added that this word is translatable—other terms used by the natives for the same creature, *mirka, yeti,* and *sogpa,* are not—and stated that *kangmi* means "snowman," while *metoh* is a term of disgust or revulsion which can be rendered as "abominable" or "foul." Though Colonel Howard-Bury himself made light of the idea of the existence of a special and unknown race of "snowmen" (he suggested that the tracks might have been wolf tracks), the daily press would have none of his explanation. A report from an expedition which was a preliminary survey for a later climb to the peak of the world's highest mountain made good copy all right, but the possibility of encountering a hitherto unknown race of "wild men"—that was a *story*! And the newspapermen did have a very good point: it was the natives' calm assertion versus Colonel Howard-Bury's guess, and although the colonel was an able and experienced man, just who had lived there all his life and could be expected to know what else lived in the same area? This, of course, has remained the argument ever since.

Actually Colonel Howard-Bury was not the first to report either on mysterious tracks or on the natives' assertion that

---

[1] In magazine and newspaper articles you can find this term in a variety of spellings, as *metoh-kangmee, metchkangmi,* and *Metch-kangmi,* substituting a "c" for an "o" in a critical place. I am following the usage of W. H. Murray, who was a member of the 1951 Reconnaissance Expedition to Everest and who seems to have some familiarity with the native tongues.

there were snowmen. The earliest source known at the moment is a book by one Major L. A. Waddell, who, on the title page, is identified as having been a member of the India Army Medical Corps. The book is entitled *Among the Himalayas*; it was published in London in 1899, but his journey—from Darjeeling to northeastern Sikkim—took place in 1889. On page 223 of the book occurs the following passage:

Some large footprints in the snow led across our track and away up to the higher peaks. These were alleged to be the trail of the hairy wild men who are believed to live amongst the eternal snows, along with the mythical white lions whose roar is reputed to be heard during storms. The belief in these creatures is universal among Tibetans. None, however, of the many Tibetans I have interrogated on this subject could ever give me an authentic case. . . .

Major Waddell, for want of a better explanation, suggested that the tracks may have been made by a bear, most likely of the species *Ursus isabellinus*.

Another, though somewhat dubious, source, which probably antedates Colonel Howard-Bury's report, is a book by a French author, Jean Marquès-Rivière. The title of his book is *L'Inde Secrète et sa Magie*—it is probably my fault that this title alone makes me wrap myself in several layers of the finest skepticism available. Monsieur Marquès-Rivière, in any event, says that a pilgrim assured him that the creatures were a race of human giants, neither bears nor monkeys, and that they spoke an unknown language. The pilgrim claimed to have been a member of an expedition of natives who followed a track of footprints and finally saw the snowmen. Ten "or more" of them sat in a circle; they were "10-12 feet high, beating tom-toms, oscillating and engaged in some magic rite. Their bodies were covered with hair; their faces between man and gorilla; quite naked at that great altitude, and a sadness expressed on their frightful visages."

Nobody is under any obligation to believe any of this, but

whether or not the witness or the writer of the book embel-
lished the story, it can be still taken as an independent report
on the existence of such a belief among the natives.

Confirmation of the universality and casual acceptance of
the belief, if it actually was still needed, came in 1922 from
the leader of the second Everest expedition, General C. G.
Bruce. When General Bruce stopped at the Rongbuk Monastery, located to the north of the mountain, he used the
opportunity to ask the Head Lama whether he had ever
heard of the metohkangmi. The Head Lama reacted to the
question as if it had been about a herd of yak or something
else equally generally known, and said, yes, five of them lived
farther up in the Rongbuk Valley.

General Bruce apparently felt that he could not spare
either the time or the manpower to go after the snowmen.
In retrospect his decision to keep to the main task looks
wrong, since Everest was not climbed then and a diversion
of forces might have led to a discovery. But in recent decades
expeditions have always had very specific and definite goals,
just as if they were military operations. This probably is a
fundamental mistake; the earlier explorers who went out to
see what they could find seem to have been more successful
on the whole. Of course it is also possible that General Bruce
simply disbelieved the whole story.

In 1925 a report appeared in Bombay, privately published
and not causing any stir discernible from a distance. Its
author was an Italian, N. A. Tombazi, who had then returned
from a photographic expedition to the southern portions of
the glacier area of the Kanchenjunga. Signor Tombazi stated
simply that he had actually seen a snowman, at an elevation
of about 15,000 feet.

Intense glare prevented me seeing anything for a few seconds,
but I soon spotted the object referred to two or three hundred
yards away down the valley—unquestionably the figure in outline
was exactly like a human being, walking upright and stopping
occasionally to uproot some dwarf rhododendron. It showed dark

against the snow and wore no clothing. Within the next minute or so it had moved into some thick scrub and was lost to view. I examined the footprints which were similar in shape to those of a man but only 6-7 inches long by 9 inches wide at the broadest part. Marks of five toes and instep were clear but trace of heel indistinct. I counted five at regular intervals from 1 to 1½ feet. The prints were undoubtedly of a biped.

A stride of 12 to 18 inches is about normal for a man who is not in a special hurry. As for the dimensions of the footprints, it might be that the heel did not touch the ground, or at least not firmly enough to leave an impression.

Just as Colonel Howard-Bury's report on mysterious tracks proved not to have been the earliest, so Tombazi's report on a sighting turned out not to be the first. An earlier one had been transmitted by one H. J. Elwes, a Fellow of the Royal Society, to the Zoological Society of London and had been published in the *Proceedings* for 1915. The actual witness was not Mr. Elwes himself, but a forest officer named J. R. P. Gent, who was stationed in the vicinity of Darjeeling and who said that he had seen humanoid creatures, called *sogpa* by the local people, above the treeline. They looked more apelike than manlike to Mr. Gent, who went on to say that they were covered with long yellowish-brown hair. Their stride measured from 1½ to 2 feet on reasonably flat ground. But in steep places they seem to "walk on their knees" so that the toe marks seem to point backward. This last remark is important if only because quite a number of people have made fun of an alleged belief of the Tibetans that the feet of the snowmen point backward.

Chronologically, a story told by the English explorer Hugh Knight lies between the Elwes–Gent report and Tombazi's publication. Unfortunately I have not been able to find Knight's original story, so that the following is very much second- or even third-hand and is given essentially for the sake of completeness. Hugh Knight is reported to have seen a snowman (who was unaware of his presence) from as close a distance as twenty paces. The snowman had the size of a big man, with a barrel chest and overlong arms. His skin was yellow and covered with blondish hair. He had the high cheekbones of the mongoloids and splayed feet. Though apparently without clothing the creature carried a primitive bow. He is reported to have suddenly run off, as if in pursuit of something which Knight could not see.

Whatever the merits of this story, the next man to write in defense of the snowmen is a famous geographer and explorer, Ronald Kaulbach. He stated that, in 1936, he had come across tracks "looking exactly as though they had been made by a barefooted man" in a pass between the valleys of the Chu and Salween rivers. There were not just one set of tracks but five of them. Kaulbach had four Sherpa porters with him. All four were agreed on the existence of the metohkangmi, but only two said that these particular tracks had been made by them, the other two were willing to admit that they *might* have been made by snow leopards. Though Kaulbach stressed that "there are no bears in that part of the country," he was told later that the tracks must have been made either by bears or by giant pandas or by an unknown species of monkeys. Kaulbach replied that neither bears nor giant pandas occur in this area, that there are no monkeys there either, and furthermore that any monkeys living there would not go above the snowline. He might have added (but didn't) that "an unknown species of monkeys" would be a very interesting discovery too.

The species of bear usually credited by far-away experts with really having made the tracks is the one known to zoologists as *Ursus arctos pruinosus*. It does occur in the Himalayas—but not everywhere, and this is a large area—and it is a large animal, growing to the dimensions of a big American grizzly. In color its fur is pale and can be nearly white, and when it is striding normally the hind feet more or less obliterate the tracks made by the front feet, producing a strange compound spoor. The telltale sign is that in addition to the five toe marks in front there are two additional marks on either side of the track, caused by the innermost and outermost toes of the hind feet.

A case of this kind of confusion was told by Frank S. Smythe in his book *The Valley of Flowers* (New York: Norton, 1949):

About four inches of snow had fallen recently, and it was obvious that the tracks had been made the previous evening after the sun had lost its power and had frozen during the night, for they were perfect impressions distinct in every detail. On the level the footmarks were as much as 13 inches in length and 6 inches in breadth, but uphill they averaged only 8 inches in length, though the breadth was the same. The stride was from 18 inches to 2 feet on the level, but considerably less uphill, and the footmarks were turned outward at about the same angle as a man's. There were the well-defined imprints of five toes, 1½ inches to 1¾ inches long and ¾ inch broad, which, unlike human toes, were arranged symmetrically. Lastly there was what at first sight appeared to be the impression of a heel, with two curious toelike impressions on either side. . . .

My photographs were developed by Kodak Ltd. of Bombay under conditions that precluded any subsequent accusation of faking and, together with my measurements and observations . . . were examined by Professor Julian Huxley, Secretary of the Zoological Society, Mr. Martin A. C. Hinton, Keeper of Zoology at the Natural History Museum [London] and Mr. R. I. Pocock. The conclusion reached by these experts was that the tracks were made by a bear. At first, due to a misunderstanding as to the exact locality in which the tracks had been seen, the bear was said to be *Ursus arctos pruinosus,* but subsequently it was decided that it was *Ursus arctos isabellinus* which is distributed throughout the western and central Himalayas. The tracks agreed in size and character with that animal and there is no reason to suppose that they could have been made by anything else.

It would be very nice, even though somewhat disappointing, if Mr. Smythe's photographs proved more than just this single case. But they do not; even though his porters had been fooled by the tracks, the Sherpas, as a rule, are well acquainted with the bear's compound spoor. Besides, it has happened that bear tracks and "snowman" tracks were found together.

More stories about strange tracks came in shortly before the outbreak of the Second World War temporarily interrupted interest in Mount Everest. In 1937 Eric Shipton and H. W. Tilman ran a survey expedition in the Karakorum. One member of their expedition and two Sherpas visited a known but remote area which is referred to as Snow Lake and promptly found tracks: "They were roughly circular, about a foot in diameter, 9 inches deep and 18 inches apart. They lay in a straight line without any right and left stagger, nor was there any sign of overlap as would be the case with a four-footed beast. The Sherpas diagnosed them as those of a yeti. . . . A few days later, in another glacier valley, bear tracks were everywhere and were quickly recognized as such by the Sherpas." Eric Shipton had seen elsewhere such circular tracks, which indicate some melting of the snow. And Tilman, who had originally considered the whole matter as a collection of silly superstitions, openly reversed his opinion.[2]

Though these circular tracks did not show any detail, it is important that they were in a straight line. Bears can't walk that way. It is true that smaller predators, like the European fox, occasionally manage to put all four of their footprints in a straight line—in Europe they say that the fox has been "stringing"; that is, you can stretch a string over the prints—but only small four-footed animals can do it. A large creature either needs legs like a camel's to produce such a track, or else it has to be bipedal.

One particular Sherpa who accompanied Shipton repeatedly must be mentioned now: Sen Tensing. He not only saw yeti prints on quite a number of occasions, he also once saw a yeti. In November 1949 a large group of Sherpas gathered

---

[2] It might be mentioned in passing that Tombazi had also been skeptical originally, referring to the yeti as a "delicious fancy" until he saw one.

in front of the Thyangboche Monastery for a religious festival. The monastery is located on a hilltop at an elevation of about 13,000 feet, not too far from Mount Everest; in fact, the mountain can be seen from the monastery. The place where the Sherpas assembled is a meadow which is bordered on one side by a forest. It was out of those trees that a yeti suddenly appeared. The nearest of the Sherpas were about 80 feet away; they said that it was of the same size as they are themselves—they average 5½ feet in height—and that its whole body, except the face, was covered with reddish-brown hair.

Because Sen Tensing was known personally to Eric Shipton, W. H. Murray, and other explorers, they saw to it that he was thoroughly questioned later in the same month. The occasion was a cocktail party at the British Embassy at Katmandu. The Sherpa was brought in, still wearing climbing boots and heavy breeches, and several Nepalese cross-examined him for half an hour. They later said not only that Sen Tensing stuck to his story all the way through but also that he could not have done so if he had not spoken the truth.

Then came the expedition of 1951, and, as W. H. Murray put it, more news of the yeti. Writing in *The Scots Magazine* (vol. LIX, no. 2, May 1953), he told the following story:

Early in November we withdrew from Everest into Sola Khombu in Nepal, and thence explored the unsurveyed ranges which lie 30-40 miles westwards. Our party split up. Shipton and Ward penetrated into the heart of the Gaurisankar range—a wild tangle of high and icy peaks—by crossing a pass of 20,000 feet, now called the Menlung La. Bourdillon and I followed them a few days later (after explorations of our own farther north). From the Menlung La we dropped 2,000 feet onto a long, westward-flowing glacier. At 18,000 feet, on its snow-covered surface we came upon the tracks of two bipeds, which were quite distinct from the tracks of Shipton and Ward. Like the latter before us, we followed the strange tracks for two miles down the glacier, because they had chosen the best route through the crevasse system. Where broad crevasses barred the way, the tracks struck sharp left or right to avoid them or dodged around little ice cliffs and pinnacles. They were the tracks of an animal using its intelligence to choose a good, safe, and therefore (in its detail) complex route. Apart from that very important observation our evidence at the best corroborates Shipton's, for the prints had been enlarged by melting and so were the round shapeless prints typical of two previous reports.

After two miles the glacier became excessively riven so the tracks diverged rightwards onto the stony morain and there we lost them. We, too, had to take to the morain. We followed it one mile to rough grazing grounds which support small herds of wild goat and sheep and presumably yetis too. On meeting Shipton and Ward we found them still in a state of subdued excitement over the tracks for they had come on them several days earlier than we, when the prints had been no more than a few hours old. Where the snow lay soft and heavy the yetis had left only the deep outline of the foot, but where it lay thin and frozen the pad marks and the five toe marks had been distinct within the print. Where the yetis had jumped the smaller crevasses the scrabble marks of their toes could be clearly seen on the far side. The prints were 6 inches wide by 12½ inches long, the gap between the prints was 9 or 10 inches. The Sherpa, Sen Tensing, who accompanied Shipton was able to identify the prints as those of two yetis. He knew well the spoor of bear and could say at once that these were not bear tracks. . . .

Eric Shipton, who had come across the tracks when they were still fresh, took a photograph, which proves that, no matter how many "yeti tracks" were really made by bears, these were decidedly not. There is no mammal known to science which leaves such tracks. And although they resemble human tracks they are as decidedly "un-human." The latter fact is important too, for in addition to the customary explanations citing two kinds of bears, loping wolves, loping snow leopards, giant pandas, and monkeys, several people have held that the snowmen were simply men: Hindu ascetics or outlaws. Of course both Hindu ascetics (who go naked or very nearly so in the snow) and outlaws do exist, but if they leave footprints they are still human footprints, about 10 inches long and at most 4 inches wide.

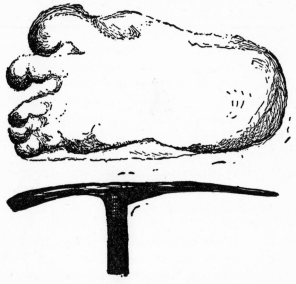

Footprint of a Tibetan "snowman" (from Eric Shipton's photograph)

The conclusion appears inevitable that the prints were made by something other than outlaws, bears, or snow leopards. W. H. Murray concluded his article rather light-heartedly by writing: "What, then, is the Abominable Snowman? In my own judgment it is no other than the metoh-kangmi, mirka, yeti or sogpa."

But what is the metohkangmi, or rather what could it be?

Before embarking on speculation I want to list quickly a few additional stories. André Roch of the Swiss expedition of 1952 reported on several sets of tracks of different sizes, as if a family had moved out of the valley when the expedition moved in. In the spring of 1954 the *Daily Mail* of London actually sent an expedition to Nepal to find the snowmen; apparently it returned empty-handed and therefore very quietly. At the same time Colonel K. N. Rana, director of the Nepalese government's Bureau of Mines, reported that on two occasions Nepalese tribesmen had actually made prisoners of snowmen. One prisoner was a baby, he was informed. The information reached him too late; a search party failed to find the people who had picked up the "snow baby"; they had simply vanished. This, it was emphasized, is not too unusual in this land of glaciers, towering peaks, and high snowy passes, but it was annoying just the same. In the other case a male snowman, presumably full-grown, was taken prisoner by tribesmen. They trussed it up securely but the specimen refused to eat what they offered and finally died on the long journey. Not realizing that a dead specimen would be almost as valuable as a live one, the tribesmen abandoned the carcass and arrived with nothing but the story of their adventure. Unfortunately for Colonel Rana mere stories are not always believed.

At the Thyangboche Monastery the Lama keeps what is declared to be the "scalp" of a yeti. In 1953 Navnit Parekh of the Bombay Natural History Society visited the monastery and was accorded by the Lama the privilege of being shown the scalp. Taking some slight advantage of the old man's friendliness, Mr. Parekh pulled out a few strands of hair, which he sent to Dr. Leon A. Hausman of New Brunswick, N. J., for examination and possible classification. Doctor Hausman tends to think that the "scalp" is actually a cap, made of fur from the back or shoulder of a large mammal. The strands of hair are definitely not from a langur monkey (*Semnopithecus roxellanae*), or from a bear, or from any animal closely related either to the langur or to the bear. The strands are quite old; their age possibly may have to be measured in terms of centuries. Finally Dr. Hausman pointed out that, if it *is* a cap, the animal which grew the fur need not be native to Nepal or Tibet.

Now, what are the snowmen?

With the aid of the track picture taken by Eric Shipton

the circle can be drawn quite tight. Obviously the creature is a mammal; the endlessly repeated assertion that it is hairy alone establishes this point. Since the size of the tracks and the length of the stride are known, the over-all size can also be determined rather closely. A stride of some 18 inches makes for a man-sized creature; a stride of 24 inches would belong to a rather tall man. A foot length of 12½ inches would also be normal for a tall man, but his feet would not be 6 inches wide and would differ considerably in shape from the ones that made the tracks. But the outline of that foot still suggests "man" in a somewhat larger sense. It suggests the "primates," the group of mammals which includes man but also the great apes and the monkeys. The last-named can be ruled out for reasons of size alone, which narrows the choice down to "man" and "ape."

Right now there are three kinds of living apes, quite different in type and appearance. Two of them live in Africa, the chimpanzee and the gorilla; the third, the orangutan, in Sumatra. All three of them, it may be important to remark, can and do assume an upright stance and walk on their hind legs only. The chimpanzee can do it better than the gorilla and the gorilla better than the orangutan. But none of them walks on his hind legs exclusively; they all revert to a special variety of four-legged walk whenever it is convenient. The mountain gorilla can stand rather cold temperatures and happens to be the least hairy of the trio, while the orangutan, on the other hand, living in the warmth of Sumatra, has exceptionally long hair, though the fur is not very dense.

One can see that the puzzle would not be completely solved simply by postulating the existence of a hitherto unknown ape of Central Asia. Not that such an ape would be impossible. Apes did live in Asia in the geologic past and they might well have shared the experience of two animals which have been mentioned in connection with "explanations" of the snowmen. Both the giant panda and the langur monkey were originally inhabitants of a near-tropical area. As the mountains slowly rose and the area cooled off, the giant panda—a fairly close relative of our raccoon—adapted to changing conditions rather than migrate elsewhere. The food problem was resolved in a somewhat peculiar manner: the panda lived exclusively on bamboo shoots. The bamboo, normally a warm-climate plant, had proved to be rather cold-resistant too. The langur monkey, itself long thought to be a fable until it was discovered by Père Armand David, also chose to remain in the cooling mountain forests, perplexing later zoologists with the surprising spectacle of a monkey roaming snowy branches, and causing itself to be actually named "snow monkey"for a while. Naturally neither of these animals lives above the snowline, where there is no food for a vegetarian or partly vegetarian animal.

What happened to the panda and the langur might also have happened to an ape. But, as I hinted a paragraph back, the supposed existence of a great ape which clung to its habitat would not fit the descriptions fully. One would have to postulate an ape with special characteristics, the most obvious of which would be the permanent adoption of bipedal walk. Why an ape, staying with his cooling forest, should have done that is hard to see; cold or not, it is still a forest. In addition, it would have to be an ape that has taken to a partly carnivorous diet, which, considering conditions, might be somewhat easier to understand. Finally, if Hugh Knight's story can be trusted, it would be the only "ape" carrying a tool around. And if one of Tilman's observations has been interpreted correctly, one yeti, on one occasion, took a pair of climbing boots from an abandoned German camp and put them to their proper use.

All this spells "man" far more clearly than it does "ape." At the moment there is a kind of scientific race being run between Asia and Africa for the honor of being the "cradle of humanity." Traditionally it was always Asia, until anthropologists and geologists started digging in South Africa and coming up with a wide variety of surprising finds. No matter whether Asia or Africa is finally acclaimed as the continent where humankind was born, the facts are that very primitive human, sub-human, and near-human creatures lived on both continents. And if a near-human and very primitive race shared the fate of the panda and the langur, its survivors would fit the descriptions of the yeti perfectly.

5: *Prelude to Aviation*

WHEN Man first began to sort out in his mind the animal life around him he found a simple and perfectly "natural" scheme. It did not even require profound thought. All one had to do was to sit at the shore of a lake and watch: it then became clear that each major "element" had its own dominant form of life. Down below the surface of the water there were the water's creatures, the fishes. Above flew the creatures of the air, the birds. And the land behind the watcher's back was the domain of its special form, the quadrupeds—today we would say mammals.

This trend of thought was not disturbed by the fact that Man himself, though a creature of the land, was not a quadruped. He considered himself detached and above the whole; this particular kind of *philosophie zoologique* had been condensed at an early date in the Bible in the injunction: ". . . replenish the earth and subdue it: and have dominion over the fish of the sea, and over the fowl of the air, and over every living thing that moveth upon the earth."

Unfortunately whoever thought of the fish as *the* creature of the water and the bird as *the* creature of the air could also think of exceptions, or rather additions, immediately. The element of the water was shared with the fishes by a multitude of crabs and clams and other unfishlike creatures. On land there were frogs and lizards and turtles and snakes along with the mammals. In the air the birds were joined by flies and honeybees, wasps and bumblebees, butterflies and moths, dragonflies and beetles. And then there was an annoying item: the bat. When flying around at dusk it looked like a misshapen bird of the night, but if you caught one and held it in your hand you were reminded of a mouse or a shrew rather than a bird. The common man tended to think in terms of such tangible evidence, as is shown by the name "flittermouse" (German: *Fledermaus*)—"flitter" meaning "rags" or "tatters"; possibly an alliterative association with "flutter" crept in too.

The early scientists did not quite accept this kind of reasoning. The flittermouse might look like a mouse, but it could fly like a bird; moreover, it was not a quadruped. The indecision about what to do with such a creature shows up very plainly in the first comprehensive books on animals, the sixteenth-century zoological encyclopedia by Konrad Gesner. He had the choice of putting the bat into volume I of his work, among the mammals, because of its fur, toothed mouth, and large external ears; or into volume III among the birds, because of its wings. The wings won; the "flittermouse" appeared in volume III, in alphabetical order, following "finch."

But Gesner did not quite let it go at that. He told the reader about his scruples: "The flittermouse," he remarked, "is the middle-animal between the bird and the mouse, so that one may truly call it a flying mouse, though it can neither be grouped with the birds or with the mice, since it has both their shapes for it has a mouse head. . . . In addition it has sawteeth in both jaws, unlike the mouse, which has two long teeth in front, but much more like a dog. . . ." I wonder just how surprised Gesner would have been if he could have been told by a modern zoologist that there is nothing "intermediate" about the bats, but that they are full-fledged mammals which evolved wings of a sort and that their ancestors were not in the least mouselike—rodents, that is—but rather like shrews.

Long after zoologists had ceased to wonder whether the

bats should be placed with the mammals or with the birds, shades of some of the old puzzled thoughts emerged again in newer and more vigorous versions. Pascal's famous comparison of knowledge with an expanding sphere which necessarily touches the unknown in more and more places by its very growth proved its validity once more. There was the problem of flight itself, which concerned not only zoologists, but anatomists and philosophers and physicists and early inventors. Even more puzzling than the problem of flight was the problem of the bird. Evolutionary thinking had taken hold in the meantime, so that the birds could no longer be regarded as a separate creation. Like everything else they must have come from somewhere; they must have had ancestors, presumably nonflying ancestors. These ancestors might even have been featherless—feathers, even more than the power of flight, are the distinguishing characteristic of birds.

As everybody knew well, there are birds that cannot fly. The geographically isolated penguins of the southern hemisphere are completely flightless, and once these southern penguins had had a northern counterpart, the equally flightless great auk. Though both had taken to swimming instead of flying, they were not related to each other. The penguins are a rather close-knit group which was isolated in another sense too; anatomists could tell from the structure of their paddle wings that their ancestors must have been flying birds once, but could not establish where and when the penguins had branched off from the main stem of the birds. As for the extinct great auk, it had numerous flying relatives still living.

Another group of flightless birds which came to mind at once was the geographically widespread type of the ostrich. This group is comprised of the emu of Australia, the cassowary of the New Guinea region, the ostrich of Africa, and the rhea or nandu of South America. All of them are large in size and heavy of body, with long, strong legs. Zoologists could not be quite certain whether the ancestors of these ostrichlike birds had given up flight for the sake of running or whether they had started out too heavy to fly and had never acquired the ability. The doubt about the ancestral ability to fly—mere uncertainty in regard to the ostrich-like birds—became a downright suspicion in regard to the small kiwi of New Zealand, although the kiwi, paradoxically, is not too heavy for flight.

But no matter whether they had given up flying, as the penguins had, or had never been able to fly, as was suspected of the kiwi, they all have feathers.

On the other side of this strange balance sheet are quite a number of creatures other than birds and insects that have acquired flight of some sort.[1]

There are the numerous species of flying fish, of which most inhabit the tropical seas but a few occur in the Mediterranean and were therefore known to the classical authors. It is an interesting sidelight that the classically learned men of northern Europe in the time preceding the period of the great voyages of exploration never made much of, say, Pliny's rather casual mention of flying fish. They were obviously somewhat doubtful—maybe the word *volans* (flying) should be interpreted as "jumping"?

Among the animals above the fishes in the evolutionary scale, the reptiles have produced two interesting attempts at flight. One is demonstrated by *Draco volans,* the "flying dragon" of Java. This fearsomely named animal is a delicate 4-inch lizard of pretty and striking coloration, equipped with a small "sail" on each side of its body. The sail is, depending on the species, semicircular or triangular in shape. It is sup-

---

[1] In 1900 one Professor Döderlein surprised everybody with a paper in which he pointed out that the ability to fly is such an important factor in the struggle for survival that 62 per cent of all the species in the animal kingdom have attained it. He took the total number of species then known as 420,000. Of these 13,000 were birds, 600 were bats, and 280,000 were insects. Most of the latter can fly, even though some, like ants and termites, do so only once during their lifetime. It should be kept in mind, however, that a fairly large number of insects should be classified as "passive fliers," for though they are able to rise into the air, they can travel appreciable distances only when aided by wind. Most mosquitoes are such passive fliers.

ported, again depending on the species, by five or six greatly elongated ribs that are even movable to the extent that the sails can be spread or folded. Though this built-in parachute is unique, the performance of the so-called flying snake (*Chrysopelaea ornata*) of India and Ceylon is even more spectacular. This green and black snake, a tree-dwelling constrictor, is capable of contracting its ventral muscles in such

The "flying dragon" of Java (*Draco volans*)

a manner that a deep longitudinal groove is formed. When taking one of its flying leaps from branch to branch the snake holds its body stiffly straight, like a stick. For many years zoologists were reluctant to accept the stories about a flying snake, but they were at last convinced by a Major Stanley Flower's account of specimens he kept in captivity, which leaped from the windows of the top floor of his house to the somewhat lower branches of a nearby tree, a distance of several yards.

The class of the mammals has produced quite a number of accomplished aviators, plus several groups of amateurs. The accomplished fliers are, of course, the 600 species of bats, ranging in size from that of a shrew to that of a small cat. The amateurs are of the type of the so-called flying squirrel, which has a wide skin fold stretching between forelegs and hind legs on each side of the body. In addition to the flying rodents of this type, there are flying marsupials built along the same lines, and, as the largest representative of this particular design, the "flying lemur," *Galeopithecus,* of which it has been said that it is not a lemur and cannot fly.

At a somewhat later date, when engineering concepts had begun to penetrate into other fields of knowledge, this list was separated by a sharp cleavage which placed all the "flying such-and-such" in one category and the bats in another. Only the bats could really fly. Only the bats, like the birds, could live up to the technical definition of flight: "to sustain themselves airborne at will for a considerable length of time, being capable of attaining a preselected point of landing at a higher level than the point of take-off." None of the others could do that, so they were classified as mere "gliders" or "parachute animals." Whether the flying fishes belonged to the one or the other category was the subject of a long-drawn-out and occasionally very spirited debate, lasting from about 1860 to 1910. The chief cause for the long duration of the argument was the difficulty of close observation, aggravated by the lack of portable movie cameras and fast film and complicated by the side issue (still unsolved) of just why these fish take to the air. But by 1910 everybody finally accepted the fact that the flying fishes are "gliders," unable to propel themselves after they leave the water. It no doubt helped to clarify issues, ideas, and concepts that Man himself learned to fly during these five decades and experienced the differences between active flight, semi-active gliding, and passive parachuting.

And during the same five decades the paleontologists, the experts on life forms of the past, succeeded in tracing at least a portion of the early history of the undisputed masters of flight, the birds.

It is self-evident that the work of the paleontologist depends to a large extent upon luck. One can help luck along a bit by digging at sites known to be rich in fossils, but one cannot predict what will be found, beyond the fact that it will be fossils from a certain period. The period in this case was the Jurassic, the middle period of the so-called Age of Reptiles, which consists, in chronological order from earliest to latest, of the Triassic, the Jurassic, and the Cretaceous periods. About 60 million years have gone by since the end of the Cretaceous period, which was itself some 65 million years long. The two preceding periods, the Triassic and the Jurassic, each lasted about 35 million years, and these periods also have in common that each was clearly divided into three subperiods; for the Triassic period this fact is even expressed in its name. The three subdivisions of the Jurassic, again in chronological order, are called Lias, Dogger, and Malm, or, simply from the color of the stone, the black, the brown, and the white Jurassic. Since the white Jurassic is the most recent of the subdivisions, a fossil imbedded in such stone must be between 125 and 135 million years old.

The classical place where "white Jurassic" could be found was in Bavaria, a little to the north of the Danube River, halfway between Munich and Nuremberg. It was a classical place in every respect—the Limes of the Roman Empire once ran through it, following more or less the course of the Danube. The Romans had early discovered that a light-colored slate of exceptional quality was to be found near a tributary of the Danube. It was hard and strong, almost impossible to break but easy to split. The Romans had used it for the *castelli* which guarded the empire against any far-reaching ideas some chieftain beyond the Limes might conceive after the third horn of mead. The first slate quarries in the mountains were worked under the supervision of the legions for their own immediate needs, both military and otherwise; archaeologists have found a Roman military bathhouse floored with such slate.

It may be supposed that the local inhabitants continued to work the quarries for their own needs after the legions left. Very little is known about the local history of the area until the time of Wynfrith of Devonshire, better known as St. Boniface, who preached in Bavaria with authorization from

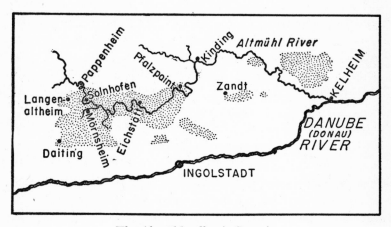

The Altmühl valley in Bavaria

Dotted areas indicate "lithographic slate" at or very near the surface

Pope Gregory II and who, in 748 A.D., became the Archbishop of Mayence. St. Boniface's connection with the white Jurassic slate is rather indirect: one of his pupils, St. Sola, went to the valley of a tributary of the Danube to live there as a hermit. Later this tributary received the name of Altmühl (Old Mill) River; it empties into the Danube at Kelheim, a short distance upstream from Regensburg. A town which is at or near the site where St. Sola lived named itself Solnhofen, which may be translated as "St. Sola's courtyard."

Solnhofen—until 1900 the name was spelled Solenhofen— later became the most famous of all the places where white

Jurassic slate was quarried, with the result that slate from the whole Altmühl Valley was often labeled Solnhofen slate. Actually the quarries of Eichstätt, Pappenheim, Zandt, Pfalzpaint, Langenaltheim, and other places in the valley are older —the Solnhofen deposits were not even discovered until 1738. Some quarries must have been in operation far back in historic times, as is proved by the slate roofs and slate floors of many very old houses in the area. We also have documentary evidence in the form of an edict, of *Fürstbischof* Marquard of Eichstätt,[2] dated 1674, regulating working conditions in the quarries of Mörnsheim, five or six miles south of Solnhofen.

The quarry owners—at Solnhofen the owner was the municipality itself—presumably considered themselves prosperous and their business thriving all through the eighteenth century. But the heavy demand for Solnhofen slate—real Solnhofen slate from the municipal quarry—was still to come. The benefactor of the city was one Aloys Senefelder, who was born in Prague in 1771. Aloys Senefelder's father was an actor; the son thought he would be a composer. In any event he wrote music. I don't know whether he tried his hand on cantatas or sonatas or fugues, but whatever it was one may have doubts about the quality, since he could not find a publisher. He decided to engrave his music himself but found the price of copper plates too high. He happened to have a slab of Solnhofen slate for mixing paints. Most likely he was unaware that the Romans had used the same kind of slate for mixing salves, but whether he knew this or not he discovered some qualities of the slate which the Romans had missed—its properties as a medium for printing. In short, he invented lithography.

The year was 1796. The news of the invention, and its use, spread rapidly, and printers also found out promptly that no other slate would do. For best results genuine Solnhofen

---

[2] The now obsolete title of *Fürstbischof*, Prince Bishop, designated churchmen who were men of the high aristocracy. They had jurisdiction over worldly affairs as well as religious matters and were sovereign over certain areas.

slate was needed. Of Aloys Senefelder it may be further mentioned that the king of Bavaria made him Royal Inspector
of Maps in 1806, that he invented color lithography in 1826,
and that he died in 1834. In Solnhofen—there is hardly another way of expressing it properly—the boom was on.
Printers and artists all over the world needed its slate and
were willing to pay for it.

Even before Aloys Senefelder became the benefactor of a
city he probably had never seen, the men who quarried slate
along the Altmühl valley had noticed that the slate occasionally showed something almost like a picture. Sometimes the
bones of a small fish could be seen, more rarely a strange
long-legged crayfish or even a dragonfly. It was only natural
that at least the better pieces were kept as curiosities. Sometimes they were sold to travelers and sometimes they were
passed on to a local priest. Gradually scientists learned about
the occasional fossils in the white Jurassic slate. Their interest, in turn, made the quarry workers and foremen more
attentive.

Thus a scientist named Collini acquired a slab of slate
with a strange fossil soon after it had been found in a quarry
at Eichstätt. The vertebrae and the neck of this fossil could
be seen clearly, one rather long leg with an apparently three-
toed foot showed up well, and there was a rather small skull
with an enormously long beak which bore tiny teeth in front
only in both the upper and lower jaws. Then there were
several long bones which probably belonged to the forelegs.
Collini did not quite know what to make of it, but in 1784
he published a description of what could be seen, calling the
fossil the remains of an "unknown marine animal."

It was the great Cuvier in Paris who realized what it was
that had been found. His first publication about it stated
even in the title that it was, or had been, *un reptile volant,*
a "flying reptile." And it was, as Cuvier suspected from the
outset and as was made definitely clear by later discoveries,
an actual *flying* reptile, not just a parachute animal like

Draco volans. Cuvier called it *Pterodactylus,* from the Greek
words *pteron* for "wing" and *daktylos* for "finger," which is
one of the comparatively few really good names in paleontology. An over-all description of the "flying finger" cannot
very well avoid comparison with the bats, especially since the
various flying reptiles of the Pterodactylus type also showed
about the same size range as the present-day bats. But there

Reconstruction of *Pterodactylus suevicus* from the Solnhofen area

In size these flying reptiles ranged from that of a sparrow to that of a raven.
Their habits must have been like those of the present-day bats, such as
sleeping with their heads hanging down

is a fundamental difference, even apart from the other fundamental fact that the bats are mammals and Pterodactylus
was a reptile. The skeleton of the bat wing shows, except for
over-all size and proportions, a surprising resemblance to a
human hand. The thumb is fairly short and usually equipped
with a strong claw; the four fingers are enormously elongated
and support the flying membrane which also encloses the
legs and the tail. Of the four long fingers the equivalent of
the index finger is usually the shortest, the equivalent of the

middle finger the longest, and the equivalent of the little finger somewhat longer than that of the ring finger. The skeleton of the Pterodactylus wing is entirely different.

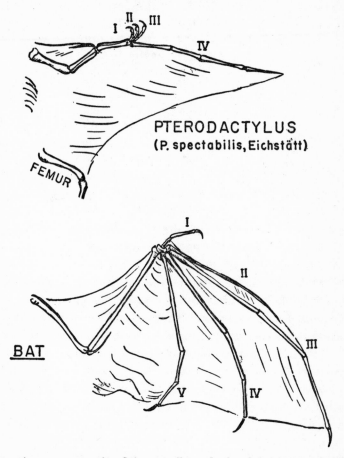

The wing structure of a flying reptile and of a flying mammal. The digits are numbered in the customary manner, so that the "thumb" is No. 1

Thumb, index finger, and middle finger are short and usually clawed; the little finger is lost, but the ring finger is longer and stronger than the bones of the arm. While, as with the bats, the flying membrane encloses arms and legs and tail, only the one finger stretches it and is, to borrow a term from aeronautics, the main wing spar.

Because of Cuvier's work the first fossil of a flying reptile to be discovered in another place than the Altmühl valley was recognized at once for what it was. This one was found in 1828 by Miss Mary Anning in the Jurassic strata of Lyme Regis in Dorsetshire. The Jurassic of Lyme Regis is black Jurassic or Lias; consequently the fossil is a good 20 million years older than the Pterodactylus from Eichstätt. It was first described in 1835 by the Very Reverend William Buckland, D.D., Dean of Westminster, who was a very fine geologist though not one of the top luminaries of this science. Dean Buckland entitled his report: *On the Discovery of a New Species of Pterodactyle in the Lias of Lyme Regis.* As this title shows, he believed it to be a fairly close relative of the type from Eichstätt, but he did point out that it had a long tail while the tail of the Bavarian specimen was ridiculously short. In fact, the tail of the Lyme Regis specimen accounted for almost half of the total length of the animal. There were also differences in body build and in skull shape.

About fifteen years later another fossil of a flying reptile turned up at Eichstätt, this time a long-tailed form from the white Jurassic. The skeleton was not quite complete but the fine-grained slate of the Altmühl valley had done something which the Lias of Lyme Regis had failed to do: it had retained the impressions made by the wing membranes. And these wing membranes had been long and narrow, of the shape of a swallow's wing, while those of Pterodactylus must have been fairly short and wide triangles. (Later finds proved this to be correct.) Most surprisingly, the long tail, thin and naked, ended in a rhomboid skin "rudder." Professor Hermann von Meyer, who described it, decided that this was not just another species of Pterodactylus but a different genus. He proposed the name of *Rhamphorhynchus.* Since the two Greek word *rhamphos* and *rhynchos* which make up this name must both be translated as "beak," a translation would read "beak of beaks." Sometimes scientific names are of that kind; the well-known swordfish of the Atlantic Ocean is *Xiphias gladius* in zoological terminology, the first part being the Greek word for sword and the second part the Latin word for the same weapon.

Professor Richard Owen in England, a famous anatomist

RHAMPHORHYNCHUS PHYLLURUS
Eichstätt (1880)

A specimen of the long-tailed flying reptiles of the late Jurassic period. The tail rudder was probably in a horizontal position when in flight. Some of the long-tailed type had a wingspread of almost 4 feet

generally regarded as Cuvier's successor in the field of pale-ontology, was a bit reluctant to accept Hermann von Meyer's name, but after re-examining the Lyme Regis specimen he fully agreed that the new find belonged to another genus. It was clear then that there had been two entirely different types of true flying reptiles during the Jurassic period. (A third type, *Pteranodon,* was later added from the American Cretaceous.) Both apparently ranged far. Since any flying animal has, of necessity, a high rate of "fuel consumption," they all need concentrated food: seeds, insects, other animals. A grass-eating flier is an impossibility; besides, the grasses did not yet exist in the Jurassic period. A lot of circumstantial evidence has led paleontologists to conclude that both Pterodactylus and Rhamphorhynchus of the Jurassic, and Pteranodon of the Cretaceous as well, led a life that can be compared with that of the fishing birds and fishing bats of our time.

With such interesting things coming to light from the slate of the Altmühl valley it is easy to understand that many scientists looked forward to new announcements as one waits for the daily mail. But in spite of much commercial quarrying the news did not come fast. If one wanders through the paleontological exhibits of a modern museum of natural history the steady repetition of the names of Eichstätt and Solnhofen may easily conjure up a picture of slate quarries stuffed with beautifully preserved and rare fossils. It would be nice if this picture were correct, but it isn't. What fools the visitor to a museum is that he momentarily forgets that he is dealing with a highly artificial concentration of remains which took a long time to accumulate. One might as well conclude after a visit to the meteorite collection of the Hayden Planetarium in New York that the earth is daily being pelted by iron meteorites weighing between 3 and 15 tons apiece.

But apparently the impression that the Solnhofen slate was about as full of fossils as a herbarium is of dried plants prevailed for some time. In 1922 the famous Viennese paleontologist Professor Othenio Abel felt obliged to issue a kind of warning. He stated that, for one thing, the municipal quarry of Solnhofen was virtually exhausted, and continued, "Whoever undertakes a trip to Solnhofen and the neighboring quarries of the Altmühl valley in the hope of finding an impressive number of beautiful and valuable fossils will be bitterly disappointed. After climbing around in the quarries for several days he might have found, especially in the vicinity of Eichstätt, a number of the free-floating crinoid Saccocoma, a few ammonites, and several Leptolepis, a small fish of about the size of a sardine, but it would be a case of very special good luck if he had found even one somewhat larger or more valuable fossil. The wealth of fossils in the slate is . . . caused by the intensity of commercial operations and the special attention of the quarry owners and all their workmen who immediately salvage every fossil which comes to light in the course of their daily labors."

The special attention which Professor Abel mentioned fortunately also existed in 1850; everybody from the owner down to the youngest apprentice was steadily on the lookout for fossils. Nothing was broken except accidentally, and then the pieces were saved; nothing was thrown away. And a special class of middlemen began to form, people who did not have any scientific training but who had acquired an eye for fossils, who knew what was relatively common and could therefore tell if something was rare, and who went around the quarries at intervals, buying up what had been found and offering their "interim collections" to scientific institutions in turn.

In 1860 a piece of slate showing a single bird feather was found. I don't know how it looked when it was taken from the Solnhofen quarry, but when I saw it on exhibit some 60 years after its discovery the slate had been neatly squared off, measuring about 5 by 7 inches, with the feather in its precise center. The size of the feather was such that it might have come from the breast of a pigeon. Within a short time the fossil came to the study of Professor Hermann von Meyer, who was understandably excited. A feather, even a single one, proved the existence of birds. Hermann von Meyer described it in the *Jahrbuch für Mineralogie* (*Annual of Mineralogy*) for the year 1861 and provided a scientific name for the bird which so far was known only by the one feather it had left in the lithographic slate. The Greek word *archaios* means "very old" and *pterinos* means "feathered"; using these words von Meyer coined the name *Archaeopteryx lithographica.*

A single feather, however, was not completely beyond what lawyers call reasonable doubt. The impression did look like a feather, but one could question it on several counts. It was of course not the feather itself which had been preserved, but its impression only—could it be the impression of a leaf which just looked like a feather? If so, it could not be considered proof of the existence of birds during the Jurassic period, since it was the *only* proof. Then, even if the impression actually was that of a feather one could not be really certain that it belonged to a bird. Anatomists were reasonably certain even then that the feather had evolved from the reptilian scale. But if this was so who could deny that at one time in the past, say during the Jurassic period, there had been feathered reptiles?

Before anybody got around to formulating elaborate theories and learned arguments the discussion was cut short by the announcement that the bird that had to go with the feather had been found, just one year after the feather. It had not come from Solnhofen but from another sector of the quarry in Langenaltheim, about one hour's walk to the west from Solnhofen. It had been bought, at an unstated price, by one Ernst Häberlein, *Landarzt* (county doctor) in nearby Pappenheim and was for sale as a part of a small collection of unusual "lithographic fossils." Until a buyer was found, Dr. Häberlein would be glad to show the fossil to any scientists who cared to come to Pappenheim. Because of the uniqueness of the find, Dr. Häberlein could not permit anyone to photograph the relic, or make drawings; he allowed only personal inspection in his presence. Of course after a sale had been made the new owner could do as he pleased. As regards the price, Dr. Häberlein felt that $4000 would be quite reasonable.

Professor Albert Oppel did not lose any time in visiting the business-minded county doctor. Of course he flinched

Archaeopteryx: first specimen, later called the London specimen

when he thought of the local equivalent of $4000, but he
himself did not intend to spend more money than the trip

would cost. Professor Oppel and Ernst Häberlein met, and after a few preliminary remarks Häberlein put the fossil on the table. It was in a slab not much larger than an ordinary piece of writing paper. There were impressions of the feathers of two wings, a long feathered tail, the skeleton of a bird's leg complete with foot. The foot of the other leg was missing, as were the skull and large portions of the body.

The finest description of what it looked like was given soon after by Professor Richard Owen. He wrote:

The remains . . . as preserved in the present split slab of lithographic stone recalled to mind the condition in which I had seen the carcase of a Gull or other seabird left on estuary sand after having been a pray to some carnivorous assailant. The viscera and chief masses of flesh, with the cavity containing and giving attachment to them, are gone, with the muscular neck and perhaps the head, while the indigestible quill-feathers of the wings and tail, with more or less of the limbs, held together by parts of the skin, and with such an amount of dislocation as the bones of the present specimen exhibit, remain to indicate what once had been a bird.

Professor Oppel looked at the slate. Häberlein was satisfied that he did not sketch it, and there were then no cameras small enough to be concealed. But to a specialist like Oppel a bone was not just a bone, it was the specific bone of a bird, dislocated from the position it should be in in such and such a manner and to such and such an extent. Examining the plate, feather for feather and bone for bone, as an anatomist would, Oppel *simply memorized it*. Then he went home and made a fine drawing.

The drawing was published by Andreas Wagner, who furnished the first preliminary description and a tentative name. Here, it seemed to Professor Wagner, was what some people had guessed at from theoretical reasoning: a feathered reptile. Some of the bones were rather birdlike but others pronouncedly reptilian. Too bad that the head was missing, but to make up for this there was the long reptilian tail. No living bird has an external tail; what is called a long tail, as in pheasants and peacocks, is simply long tail feathers. The actual bony tail of a bird is inside the body, and usually a number of tail vertebrae are even fused into a special bone, called the plowshare bone, which is the support for the tail feathers. To Wagner the long tail alone was proof of the essentially reptilian nature of the fossil.

Andreas Wagner would have liked to go to Häberlein's residence himself for a personal examination of the fossil, but he was too sick to travel—he died soon afterward—and had to rely on Oppel's drawing and personal report. Since a feathered reptile reminded him of the mythological griffin which is customarily drawn as something like a feathered dragon, he named the fossil "griffin-lizard," *Griphosaurus.* A zoologist named Giebel was the only one to contradict sharply; everybody else had the good sense to wait until more became known. Giebel declared the whole thing an absurdity. Feathers, he said, were feathers and scales were scales. And lizards are lizards and birds are birds. So if this plate shows lizard bones it is a fossil lizard. It cannot show feathers too because lizards don't have feathers. But if it does show feathers the feathers must be faked. And science does not deal with fakes, except to expose them. Now that he, Giebel, had exposed this fake, let's get back to genuine fossils.

Meanwhile Richard Owen, who a few years earlier had been appointed superintendent of the Natural History Section of the British Museum, quietly discussed with the trustees the desirability of owning the fossil. The trustees nodded agreement; if Professor Owen said it was desirable, then of course it was desirable. Owen sent a Fellow of the Zoological Society, a Mr. Waterhouse, to Bavaria to inspect Häberlein's collection, of which the bird fossil was the most important piece. Mr. Waterhouse returned and said that it was worth the price (which had been reduced a bit in the meantime) and the British Museum sent a bank draft for £600 to Häberlein. A few German scientists did not like the

idea that the unique specimen had gone to London, but none
of them, or the institutions they represented, had the equivalent of $3000 liquid and ready. Richard Owen, in any event,
could be trusted to produce the best scientific description
possible.

Richard Owen did. His report *On the Archeopteryx of
von Meyer* appeared in 1863[3] and made it clear once and for
all that there had been a bird in Jurassic times. Owen compared it in size with the peregrine falcon, and (this more by
accident) the one foot matched the foot of the peregrine
falcon best both in size and in shape. In spite of the long tail
and the reptilian cast of a number of the bones, Owen was
convinced that this was a true bird. A bird with reptilian
characteristics, yes, but a flying bird, not just a feathered
reptile. Since it was indubitably a bird Owen rejected
Wagner's name of *Griphosaurus—sauros* being the Greek
word for lizard—and re-established von Meyer's name, Archaeopteryx. But since the single feather which had been found
in 1860 did not match any of the feathers on the London
specimen, as it came to be called, Owen thought that the
feather had belonged to a different species. Since Solnhofen
and vicinity had yielded both short-tailed and long-tailed
flying reptiles, Owen said that the area might also yield short-
tailed and long-tailed Jurassic birds. Possibly the single
feather came from a short-tailed bird which, when found,
would take von Meyer's full name *Archaeopteryx lithographica*. The London specimen was most obviously long-
tailed (*macrura* in Greek) and should be called *Archaeopteryx
macrura*.

Richard Owen had spoken the last word for a long time
in matters relating to Archaeopteryx, largely because he had
said everything that could be said. Only old Professor Giebel
kept remarking that all this was nonsense, nobody had ever

[3] In *Philosophical Transactions of the Royal Society of London for the year
MDCCCLXIII*, vol. 153, pt. 1, pp. 33-47, with several beautiful (lithographic)
plates.

seen either a feathered lizard or a long-tailed bird, and this was just a case of one Englishman trying to prove another Englishman (meaning Darwin) right—something that wasn't Owen's intention at all. Giebel's colleagues grew annoyed at times, but in general they let him talk and waited—for another Archaeopteryx, one that had not been three-quarters eaten by something else. And, if one could make a wish, one with a head.

The years went by and there were all kinds of developments. Scientific discoveries were made: one could now tell the chemical elements composing the stars just by analyzing their light. Technology progressed: the telegraph and the railroad became common. There were political changes: the German states fought France and a German empire resulted. In the more specialized field of paleontology a new name and a new continent began to intrude: Professor Othniel C. Marsh in America sent the most amazing reports about the most incredible fossils he had discovered in the American West. But still no new Archaeopteryx.

Finally, in 1877, Herr J. Dürr, owner of a quarry near Eichstätt, found a slab of slate which was imperfect from the point of view of a builder. At one corner a piece had split off so that the slab had only about half its thickness there. But on the exposed inner surface something like a small bunch of feathers showed. In some never-explained manner Ernst Häberlein learned about this fossil at once and bought the piece from Dürr for a never-revealed price. Then he went home and with the skill that he had acquired in many years split the slate to expose the imbedded fossil. It was an Archaeopteryx, complete with head! At first glance it even looked as if it were complete in every detail. Later examination did not support this view; a few minor portions were missing and had presumably been eaten by crabs. But it certainly was a much better specimen than the one for which Professor Owen had paid £600.

Häberlein's reasoning was simple-minded and straightforward. This was a much better specimen; therefore it ought to be more valuable. Translating his thought into the new unified currency of the new German Empire, he asked for 36,000 marks ($8560), on the usual simple conditions. It was to be a tie-in sale as before, meaning he would add a small collection of other lithographic fossils as a friendly bonus. No drawings or photographs were to be made, but accredited scientists representing scientific—preferably solvent—institutions were invited to inspect the find. Häberlein probably had in mind to see to it that these inspections did not last too long, just in case somebody with the memory and artistic ability of Professor Oppel should appear.

At various institutions there were conferences between scientists and trustees. In London not much mental arithmetic was needed; Häberlein's new price amounted to an even £1800. The British Museum decided to say nothing for a while. When a representative of a Munich museum said to Häberlein that the price was somewhat high, Häberlein replied that he was a reasonable man; in fact, he was just contemplating an offer from Professor O. C. Marsh of Yale University of just $7500. (Whether Marsh ever made such an offer is not known.) Häberlein felt quite secure in his position. He could count on various factors. The British Museum, having bought the first specimen, would certainly like to have the second one too. And the British Museum had money. As for Professor Marsh in America, it was hard to guess just how deeply he would be interested in a European specimen, but Professor Marsh had worked on fossil birds of lesser age from American sites—and the Americans had money. Häberlein's main trump card, however, was just the fact that the first specimen had been sold to the British Museum. German scientists would do everything to keep Number 2 in Germany.

Häberlein's reasoning proved to be perfectly correct.

There was a foundation in Frankfurt-on-the-Main—it bore the untranslatable name of *Freies deutsches Hochstift*—which had the purpose of saving German antiquities and items of historical interest. It had, for example, saved Johann Wolfgang von Goethe's house in Frankfurt from destruction by the simple expedient of buying it. Although the foundation was not normally interested in fossils, the second Archaeopteryx was obviously a special case. Moreover, the chairman of the foundation, Dr. O. Volger, happened to be a geologist. The foundation did not have the money on hand, but Dr. Volger approached Häberlein, and they signed a contract which stipulated that the foundation would take the specimen under its care for a period of six months. During these six months the foundation would either raise the money for a direct purchase or else would act as an agent for another German institution or foundation. The other conditions were those Häberlein had always made: no drawings, no photographs, no casts.

Contract signed and specimen under his care, old Dr. Volger first approached the German government. But there were difficulties. The German Empire was deeply interested, Dr. Volger was told. But it was a new empire and therefore had no equivalent of the British Museum—no Empire Museum so to speak. But the Empire was a federation of kingdoms, principalities, etc., and these had museums of their own. The discussions with officials of the German Empire no doubt enriched Dr. Volger's knowledge of constitutional and administrative principles and problems, but that was all. The alternative seemed to be to raise the 36,000 marks from various sources, but the six months ran before even a fraction of the sum had been pledged.

Häberlein was asked whether he would grant an extension of the agreement for another three months. Häberlein agreed, but Dr. Volger was still unable to get the money. Häberlein, after waiting a few more months, took his specimen back with him to Pappenheim and started to negotiate directly. At first he corresponded with the University of Geneva. The man in charge of the department of geology was old Professor

Karl Vogt, a German exile for political reasons and a devoted
follower of Darwin. There was no doubt that Karl Vogt
wanted the fossil, but the university simply did not have that
much money. Next Häberlein approached the museum in
Munich. Since Archaeopteryx had actually been found in
Bavaria, the people in Munich, the capital of Bavaria, were
most interested—one might even say that to them it was more
a question of regional patriotism than of scientific prestige.
But they did not have enough money either.

Häberlein wrote to Berlin, which was a dual capital, of
the German Empire and of the Kingdom of Prussia. After
he had been rejected twice because the price was too high—
and Häberlein knew that this was really the reason—he
decided not to risk a third rejection on those grounds. He
asked for 26,000 marks. And, having learned about Dr.
Volger's negotiations, he approached an institution of the
Kingdom of Prussia: the Royal Mineralogical Museum of
the University of Berlin. Its paleontological collection was
not impressive at that time and Berlin was eager to acquire
such a unique find. But no matter how eager the curator
might be, there was a procedure to be followed, especially
when such a large sum was involved. The Museum had to pass
its recommendation on to the University, and the University
had to pass it on to the place the money came from, namely
the Royal Prussian Ministry of Education. And the Ministry
had its own procedure, which required, first of all, expert
testimony about the genuineness and the value of the items
to be purchased. Privy Councilor Professor Dr. E. Beyrich
was delegated to travel to Pappenheim, examine the collection, and report.

It would have been difficult at that time to find a paleontologist, geologist, or zoologist anywhere in the world who
had a kind word to say about Ernst Häberlein. The second
Archaeopteryx had been found in 1877. Privy Councilor
Beyrich traveled to Pappenheim early in April 1880. Three
years had gone by and all anybody knew was that the thing

existed. No description was available, not even a picture. And Häberlein, while negotiating with the Prussian Ministry of Education, continued to negotiate with America, or at least said he did. During the same week that Dr. Beyrich spent in Pappenheim examining the fossils somebody told the story to the industrialist Werner von Siemens, famous designer of electrical equipment and part owner of the gigantic Siemens and Halske factories. He listened, asked a question or two about the value, and acted.

Within a few days Ernst Häberlein accepted 20,000 marks in cash and disappeared from the scene; he presumably retired. The fossil was now the private property of Werner von Siemens who immediately made a formal offer to the Berlin museum at the price he had paid himself. And a month or so later scientists could at long last go to work on it.

Even those brief glances that some of them had caught of the fossil while Häberlin was holding out for a high price had shown to them that it—the Berlin specimen, as it soon came to be called—was not quite the same as the London specimen. It was generally smaller, about the size of a pigeon, and less sturdily built. There were other differences too, and it therefore had to have a different name, which fact, I am sorry to report, caused some more trouble. The Germans had never ceased to call the London specimen *Archaeopteryx lithographica,* the name Owen wanted to reserve for the single feather. The name of *Archaeopteryx siemensi* was proposed for the Berlin specimen to honor Siemens for his fast and successful action. But there were a few opposing voices—Siemens had been reimbursed, hadn't he?—and the next suggestion was to accept Owen's *Archaeopteryx macrura* for the London specimen and to establish *Archaeopteryx lithographica* for the Berlin specimen. This suggestion was disregarded because it would have led to hopeless confusion. Later the problem of the name resolved itself when it was established that the differences between the London and Berlin specimens were sufficient to warrant a different generic name. The Berlin specimen was called *Archaeornis*, "ancient bird"—but only *after* most of the important papers about it had appeared with Archaeopteryx in the title.

Archaeornis was examined down to the minutest possible detail at least three times, the first description coming from Wilhelm Dames, who worked in Berlin.[4] Archaeornis and Archaeopteryx were alike in many features—always keeping in mind that Archaeopteryx is somewhat larger and more sturdily constructed. For example, the one foot of Archaeopteryx that is preserved is larger and stronger beyond the difference in scale; it must have had more grasping power than the feet of Archaeornis. But the feet of the two specimens are alike in construction in that, though looking quite similar to a bird's foot of the present, they are actually closer to the construction of the feet of some reptiles. Both Archaeornis and Archaeopteryx have the same long reptilian tail, that of Archaeopteryx having twenty-one vertebrae, that of Archaeornis only twenty; both have the same type of vertebrae, which even among reptiles can be found only in old forms, as, for example, in the still-living Hatteria of New Zealand. Archaeornis showed ventral ribs, also an ancient reptilian attribute (Hatteria has them); as to Archaeopteryx, it was impossible to be sure, since the specimen had been too mutilated—and had also partly decayed before fossilizing.

While Archaeopteryx had clearly displayed the feathered long tail and bunches of feathers showed where the wings had been, Archaeornis gave information about most of the

[4] W. Dames, *Ueber Archaeopteryx;* Paläontologische Abhandlungen, Bd. II, 1884. *Ueber Brustbein, Schulter- und Beckengürtel der Archaeopteryx;* Sitzungsberichte der kgl. preuss. Berlin: Akademie der Wissenschaften, 1897.
Other important publications are:
W. P. Pycraft, "The Wing of Archaeopteryx," *Natural Science,* 1894, no. 33 and 34; 1896, no. 50.
G. Heilmann, *Fuglenes Afstamning.* Copenhagen, 1916 (published in English as *The Origin of Birds,* New York: D. Appleton, 1927).
B. Petronievics, *Ueber die Berliner Archaeornis.* Geneva, 1925.
Gavin de Beer, *Archaeopteryx lithographica: A Study Based on the British Museum Specimen.* London: British Museum (Natural History), 1954.

plumage. The wings were virtually intact and it could be seen that the legs had been feathered too. There was a clear ruff of feathers around the base of the neck. The neck itself

Archaeornis: the Berlin specimen

seemed naked, and as for the body it was at first difficult to decide. Old Professor Karl Vogt in Geneva, who had wanted to buy Archaeornis, was much impressed with this information. Feathers showed on tail, legs, and wings, but nowhere else except for that ruff around the base of the neck—this, he mused, probably meant that body and neck had been covered by scales. Maybe, he said, Andreas Wagner had been right after all and the animal had actually been a feathered lizard. But Wilhelm Dames and later Gerhard Heilmann contradicted this, pointing out that if you looked at the original instead of at photographs you could make out where the body feathers had been.

Archaeornis as it probably looked in life, shown eating the seeds of
a cycad tree

The wings were one of the features in which Archaeornis differed most from modern birds. There were still three "fingers," with large claws which must have been helpful in climbing on the rough trunk of a cycad tree. But Heilmann could show that two of the three fingers had grown together in a highly surprising manner; they could not have been as freely movable as had originally been thought. Of all living birds only the South American hoatzin still develops something like that for a while when young. As William Beebe

and others have observed, the wing claws of the young hoatzin
do help in climbing. The wing fingers of Archaeornis probably could not do much better; as Heilmann wrote, "Nature's attempt at producing an organ for both climbing and
flying purposes seems to have been anything but successful

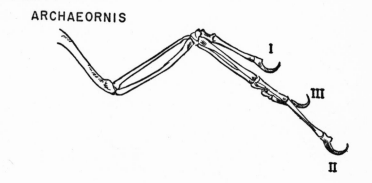

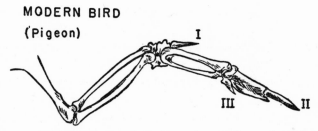

The wing bones of *Archaeornis* and of a modern bird

Note how the second and third "finger" of *Archaeornis* are connected and that
the same bones in the wing of a present-day bird are reduced to small stubs

and it is not surprising that the grasping power of the wing
was lost."

That the flying power of the Archaeornis wing was not
too advanced was obvious almost at first glance. Not only
are the wings small compared to the body size; they could
not have had much power behind their strokes. Archaeornis
still lacked the enormously developed breastbone of the
modern birds, which is the anchor for the flying muscles.

Nobody doubts that Archaeornis had the power of true flight, but the flight must have been fairly slow, the wing strokes "weak," and the duration of each flight rather short. That the feathered legs helped, that they were "pelvic wings," was for a while a minority opinion of one man, but was discredited by Othenio Abel and fully demolished by Gerhard Heilmann. If the legs had been "pelvic wings" they could never have assumed the position in which they show in the fossil.

Last but not least, Archaeornis demonstrated the type of head those early birds possessed. It was a small head with little room for a brain and without the horny bill so typical for all living birds. And it still bore a large number of tiny sharp teeth. From the size of its mouth it is quite evident that Archaeornis must have fed on either insects or seeds, or perhaps both. But its powers of flight were not sufficient to catch on the wing the dragonflies which are so well known from the Solnhofen slate; the insects it ate must have been crawling insects.

The head of Archaeornis has been the subject of a highly enlightening disagreement among the experts. Wilhelm Dames called it "all bird," except for the teeth. Gerhard Heilmann, on the other hand, stressed all its reptilian characteristics and gave a drawing of the skull he had made directly from the fossil, accompanied by drawings of the skulls of two extinct reptiles, *Aëtosaurus* and *Euparkeria*. He could show that they matched bone for bone, and not only could the corresponding bones of one skull be found in both the others, but they even differed little in shape and had the right proportional sizes. Heilmann proved his point, of course, but Dames's slip goes to show that even the skull of a modern bird still shows a good many reptilian characteristics. In general, Heilmann concluded that Dames's original contention—that "Archaeornis was already a bird but still endowed with many reptilian features"—was wrong, although it had been accepted by most zoologists at the time it was made. Instead, Heilmann wrote, "We may now stop talking about the 'missing link' between birds and reptiles, so much so is Archaeornis this link that we may term it a warm-blooded reptile disguised as a bird."

It was just this comparison of the skull of Archaeornis with those of two extinct reptiles which shed much light on the ancestry of Archaeornis and the ancestry of the birds in general. These two reptiles, *Aëtosaurus ferratus* from the Triassic period of Europe and *Euparkeria capensis* from the

Reconstructed head of *Archaeornis,* actual size. The long feathers of the crest are *not* indicated on the fossil, but are a likely adornment of the male at mating time

Triassic of South Africa, belonged to the same order, now extinct as a whole. The order bears the name *Pseudosuchia,* and when it was still thriving there existed another, now also completely extinct order of reptiles called the *Parasuchia.* The names may be translated as "pseudo-crocodiles" and "para-crocodiles." Paleontologists suspect that both branched from the same stem, the para-crocodiles adapting to life in water, the pseudo-crocodiles to life on land. The order of the crocodiles, still well represented by living forms, probably sprang from the pseudo-crocodiles, which were rather pro-

lific. Quite a number of spectacular later "dinosaurs" are
known to have evolved from the pseudo-crocodiles. So did
the flying reptiles of the types Pterodactylus and Rhamphorhynchus. And so did the birds.

In old books with titles like "Marvels of the Fossil World,"
written at a time when little was known and that imperfectly,
you can find remarks to the effect that the flying reptiles were
somehow on their way to becoming birds; these remarks
sound rather like Gesner's statement that the bat is the
middle-animal between the birds and the mice. Of course in
this form the statement is nonsense. Pterodactylus, after it
had grown its wing membrane, did not sprout feathers. And
the ancestors of the birds that did sprout feathers never had
a wing membrane. Indeed, for many millions of years the
membrane must have seemed the better solution; Rhamphorhynchus was obviously a far better flier than Archaeornis.
But the old, mistaken thought happened, by sheer accident,
to contain a grain of truth; the flying reptiles and the birds,
though going, or rather flying, their strictly separated ways,
both came from the same ancestral group of reptiles, the
pseudosuchians.

The reptiles belonging to the line that led to the birds
must have acquired a more or less bipedal walk, with the
forelimbs thus left free for other tasks, and have had the
feet modified in such a manner that they resembled bird feet
in appearance. But we know from countless fossil examples
that the reptiles which took to walking on their hind legs
only—either to widen their horizon in the literal optical
meaning of the word, or for greater speed—simply had their
forelimbs reduced because they did not make *any* use of
them. It is obvious therefore that the pseudosuchians which
were to become the ancestors of the birds must have been
bipedal but must have used their forelimbs vigorously just
the same. This could happen only with tree-dwelling forms
which had a need for grasping hands—*and* for a parachute.
Of course only small animals can be tree dwellers, but most

pseudosuchians known to science were small, some tiny.

The pseudosuchians used by Heilmann for skull compari-
sons were found in deposits from the "upper" (which is the
same as "late") Triassic period; Archaeopteryx and Archaeornis come from the upper Jurassic. They are roughly 40
million years apart in time, during which interval the evolution of the birds must have taken place. The same interval,
incidentally, applies to the evolution of the flying reptiles
too. The conquest of the air occurred during the earlier part
of the Jurassic period.

So far the luck which paleontologists unfortunately need
has failed to produce a specimen of "pro-avis," the name
used by Heilmann for the "feathered reptile" (more or less
what Professor Wagner thought Archaeopteryx to be) that
preceded Archaeornis. Nor have we yet found a form between
Archaeornis and the modern birds.[5] Nor, for that matter,
another Archaeopteryx or Archaeornis.

For a while it was believed that at least tracks made by
one of them were known; that is, some fossil tracks found at
Pfalzpaint and elsewhere in the Altmühl valley were ascribed
to them. One reason was that the size was about right; the
distance between the left and the right foot is almost precisely 2 inches. The other reason is best expressed by the
phrase, the wish is father to the thought. If no additional
Archaeornis was forthcoming, tracks at least would be something. These tracks sometimes, but not always, show an impression made by a tail, which means that they must have
been made by an animal which could either drag its tail
or carry it off the ground to balance the body. This seems
unlikely for Archaeornis, and it is now generally accepted
that the tracks were probably made by a small bipedal
dinosaur.

[5] Bird fossils are the rarest of all fossils, which, considering the lightness
and smallness of bird bones, is easy to understand, though regrettable.
Logically enough, the bird fossils which we do know from the Cretaceous and
Tertiary periods belong to large-bodied, swimming or walking types which
teach us nothing about the evolution of bird flight subsequent to Archaeornis.

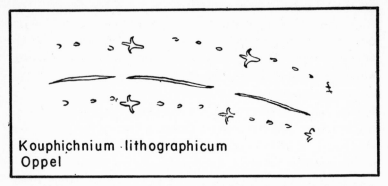

Kouphichnium·lithographicum Oppel

Fossil animal tracks from the shore of the Solnhofen bay of the Jurassic period. The long lines in the center must have been made by a dragging tail, but the spoor of the tail is not always present

One question that has been much discussed while the paleontologists have been waiting for more fossils of early birds was how the area of the Altmühl valley looked at the time the fossils were formed. The general geography of the upper Jurassic period in Europe was no mystery. The Alps did not yet exist, and over most of southern Europe rested a warm ocean, something like an enormously enlarged Mediterranean Sea, called the Tethys Sea. Europe was an archipelago of islands, most of them small, which clustered more thickly the farther north they were. What is now Scandinavia was the "mainland," or, better, the biggest of the European islands. The area of the Altmühl valley must have been a dried-up lagoon near the shore of an island of fairly respectable size. To the south of the lagoon a barrier reef had been built by corals. Some distance from the lagoon—farther inland or on separate nearby islands?—grew cycad and araucaria trees. And somewhere nearby must have been extensive dunes of coral sand, the warm winds blowing dust from these dunes over the wide expanse of the dry lagoon.

It seems a strange thought at first, but it does make sense if you think it out in detail, that the area which has given us the best-preserved fossils in existence must have been itself lifeless at the time. Remember that the fossils, though fantastically detailed, are comparatively rare. Nothing grew on the large white expanses of the Altmühl lagoon. Every once in a while, possibly as a result of a submarine earthquake, the sea washed across the coral reef, and the wave carried sea life with it, the then common free-floating crinoids, a swarm of the small leptolepis fishes, a few crabs, and a few ammonites, shelled cuttlefish. All of them were doomed to die as the water receded. But for a short time the same wave had changed the expanse of coral dust into sticky mud, from which a dragonfly which had alighted on it could not rise again. We have a fossil of a small horseshoe crab, which one can clearly see must have threshed around with its tail spike while dying. We have another fossil of a small lizard-shaped reptile, measuring a little less than 8 inches, which left a clear impression of its body, then, with a blow of its long tail, freed itself, but, falling on its left side, buried its left limbs so deeply in the mud that it could not free itself again. The leptolepis fish usually have the positions of fish which, frantically trying to reach water again, suffocated in the fine dust that was blown from the dunes.

The condition of the various fossils fits into this explanation. The sea forms are always intact; they may be in positions resulting from the death struggle of suffocation, but no parts are missing. But the land forms—the occasional small dinosaur, the specimens of flying saurians, and of course the two birds—as a rule show signs of violence. They did not succumb to the sticky mud as did the fish and the octopi; they look as if they had been already dead when they were deposited on the mud. In short, they had been killed by a larger predator who for some reason abandoned its prey. Or were they dead bodies of land animals that had found a violent death out on the barrier reef and had been washed into the dry lagoon alongside the still-living sea creatures?

It is significant that decay prior to fossilization has been observed in almost all specimens of land forms and very rarely in specimens of animals that normally live in the sea. The decay, like the death, must have taken place elsewhere, before the bodies were transported into the normally dry lagoon where mud and dust quickly covered what was left.

Part Two

BOTANICAL INTERLUDE: THREE FABULOUS TREES

And the Lord God planted a garden eastward in Eden . . . and out of the ground made the Lord God to grow every tree that is pleasant to the sight, and good for food; the tree of life also in the midst of the garden, and the tree of knowledge of good and evil.

Genesis 2:8-9

6: The Tree of Death

MARVELOUS were the things that early travelers returning from the American tropics had to tell to their relatives and neighbors (and even to their superiors) who had stayed behind in Europe. Incredible were the sights they had seen. Where they had been, somewhere on the "Isle of Prezilia," there had been tiny birds encrusted with rubies and emeralds—or at least what seemed to be jewels; the birds had been too swift to be caught—that never sat down on branches but hovered in midair, sipping nectar from flowers. They might even have had no feet. The travelers had seen centipedes large enough to attack and overpower small lizards. There the trees were in foliage all year round and they were covered with vines that bore blossoms unceasingly. The travelers had seen butterflies large enough to cover most of a folio volume if they spread their wings. And beetles giving off such a bright light that three of them, imprisoned in a clear glass bottle, made a lamp by which to read the folio. The crabs at the shore were red while alive without having been boiled, and farther out in the sea the very fish left their own element and flew, fast and glittering with wetness, through the air.

If the listeners who had stayed home where the trees shed their foliage and where the birds sat down to eat were doubtful at first, their doubts were in time crushed by evidence. The travelers brought with them dried beetles as large as small mice. They hauled sea shells of such size that they could be—and usually were—used as baptismal fonts in churches. They brought blocks of wood, which obviously were wood for they could be sawed, if with difficulty, but which would sink in water. As far as the most incredible miracle, the flying fish, were concerned, priests who had been there as missionaries solemnly asserted that they had seen these. More than that, they had held such fish in their hands after they had fallen on deck of the ship. In fact, they had eaten them afterward.

In short, it happened so often that a tale, though exceedingly strange on the face of it, was proved to be true, that nobody, on the strength of reasoning and logic alone, could hope to discover an occasional falsehood. And whether the sailor went westward across the Atlantic Ocean to the newly discovered lands, or sailed south to round the Cape of Good Hope and turn east to the long-known Indies, he would bring back tales about strange people, strange customs, and even stranger facts of Nature which you had better believe if you wanted to be on the safe side. And from both ends of the world, from the Sunda Islands in the extreme East and from the equally tropical islands in the West which all still bore Spanish names, there came tales of poisonous trees, trees of death.

I have the feeling—though I lack proof so far—that these stories about a tree of death not only produced pleasurable shudders for the ignorant but also delighted the philosophically minded. The Bible, as anyone could read—*if* he could read—in the Book of Genesis spoke of a Tree of Life which grew in the Garden of Eden. In fact, Adam and Eve, after they had eaten from the Tree of Knowledge, were banished from the Garden so that they might not eat from the Tree of Life. But the philosophically minded bookworms knew that everything in Nature had its opposite. Light opposed darkness; material things were either hot or cold, dry or wet. The lion was the king of the beasts, but there also was the awful basilisk which lived underground and could kill with a glance. A Tree of Death, reported to exist in the vast distance, almost seemed a philosophical necessity after the statement in the Bible that the Tree of Life had grown in Paradise and presumably still grew there, even though nobody could tell to which place Paradise had been removed by the Lord.

So nobody doubted the stories of the deathly tree, whether they came from the East or from the West.

The one in the West was called by a variety of names that all had a similar sound—presumably the attempts of different kinds of Europeans to imitate an Indian name. The English versions are *manchineel* or *manzanillo,* the French is *mancenillier,* the German *Manzanilla.* The tree itself was described as beautiful and inviting in appearance, sometimes decorated with fine-looking fruit resembling apples. But the natives knew that it was poisonous and were not deceived by its appearance.

> If rests the traveller his weary head,
> Grim Mancinella haunts the mossy bed,
> Brews the black hebenon, and, stealing near,
> Pours the curst venom in his tortured ear.

These lines are from a long poem called *Loves of the Plants,* written in 1789,[1] by Erasmus Darwin, M.D., grandfather of the famous Charles Darwin. The somewhat fierce and aggressive-looking Dr. Erasmus Darwin did not live long enough to see the boy baby who would later make the family's name known the world over, for Erasmus died in 1802 and Charles was not born until 1809. It is fact, however, that Erasmus Darwin's writing foreshadowed some of the thoughts which were later developed by Charles; grandfather's thoughts may have directly influenced grandson by showing that such ideas could be harbored.

While Dr. Erasmus Darwin liked to tell natural facts in

---

[1] The *Loves of the Plants* became the second part of a book entitled *The Botanic Garden.* Its first part, *Economy of Vegetation,* was written after the *Loves,* in 1792.

a poetic form he evidently did not think that his contemporaries and potential readers had enough botanical knowledge to understand his references and allusions. Therefore *The Botanic Garden* is equipped, as proclaimed on its title page, "With Philosophical Notes," taking the physical shape of footnotes in prose which take up more space by far than the poem itself. The "philosophical note" to the lines quoted read:

Hippomane.
    With the milky juice of this tree the Indians poison their arrows; the dew-drops which fall from it are so caustic as to blister the skin and produce dangerous ulcers; whence many have found their death by sleeping under its shade.

To set the facts straight right here, Dr. Darwin would still be perfectly right if he had only put a period after the word "skin" and proceeded to the next footnote. The tree now labeled *Hippomane mancenilla,* which grows in the West Indies, does produce a poisonous juice, both in its trunk and in its fruits. The juice does cause blisters on unprotected skin and it was used by the Indians to poison their arrows. Presumably—I lack definite information on this point —it would not be advisable to eat the fruit, for a poison that is dangerous when brought into the bloodstream *and* that blisters the skin is also likely to be "not for internal use." But that a person who went to sleep in its shade did not wake up again because of the "exhalations" of "Grim Mancinella" only happened in books.

    And on the opera stage!

    Giacomo Meyerbeer, né in Berlin in 1791 as Jakob Liebmann Beer, first studied and performed (as a pianist) in Berlin and Vienna. Then he went to Italy, where he composed operas that sounded a good deal as if they had been written by Rossini, and then he went to Paris, where he settled down for two decades until called back to Berlin to be the musical director of the Royal Opera. This was in 1842. Now the

Herr Generalmusikdirektor was not only supposed to select, rehearse, and conduct operas and an occasional concert, he was also expected to compose himself. Meyerbeer had been called to Berlin not only because he was a native son, but because he had written operas in Italian and in French. Now he wrote marches and cantatas and an opera to be sung in German. In between he composed another opera for the Paris Opéra, entitled *L'Africaine*. In the last act of that opera the heroine decides to die, which she does in a decorous manner by seeking out a *mancenillier* and reposing in its shade. When the opera was first performed, in 1865, one year after Meyerbeer's death, the assembled Parisians, with a sprinkling of British and German tourists, found this a most touching and very original end. Not one of them thought to inquire whether there was such a tree and whether it grew where the libretto of the opera said it did.

Interestingly enough, the use of the story on the opera stage, with full orchestra for musical background, also marked its end. No later writer could use it without being accused of having swiped from the libretto of *L'Africaine*.

But there was still the other tree of death, the one that grew in the Far East. Upas tree was its name and it was so dreadful that the manchineel seemed a wan shadow by comparison. The upas tree owes its horrible fame mostly to one man, and strangely enough we do not really know who this one man was.

But let's pursue the story in its chronological order.

The first man I know of who mentioned the poisonous tree of Java, though not by name, was quite factual about it. He was Friar Oderich of Pordenone. At the age of 32, in 1318, he embarked on a missionary journey to the Far East, from which he returned in 1330. The manuscript about his journey contains the statement: "In this land [Java] there are trees yielding meal, honey, and wine, and the most deadly poison in all the whole world. Against this poison there is but one remedy. . . ."

Friar Oderich's manuscript was later filched *in toto* by somebody who is known as Sir John de Mandeville, the author of one of the most widely read of older travel books. "Sir John"[2] died in 1372 at Liège and probably was not an English knight at all, but a French physician by the name of Jean de Bourgogne. The French doctor had actually traveled as far as Egypt and other countries in that general vicinity, and those portions of his book are based on personal experience. For the rest he ruthlessly plagiarized anybody who had written about countries farther east, from Eratosthenes and Pliny the Elder among the classics to near-contemporaries like John of Pian de Carpini, Marco Polo, the German knight Wilhelm von Boldensele, and, as mentioned, Friar Oderich. Although "John de Mandeville" eagerly looked for any marvelous tale that could be copied, the upas tree did not yet get any embellishment. He had only Oderich's sentence to go by, and this, in the Middle-English version of his book, took the following form:

And there ben other Trees, that beren hony, gode and swete; and other Trees that beren Venym; azenst the whiche there is no Medicyne but on [one]; and that is to taken here propre Leves, and stampe hem [them] and tempere hem with Watre, and than drynke it.

Most restrained indeed, especially if you keep in mind who wrote it. He would have done much better if only he had known about the *Epistolae* and the *Mirabilia* of his contemporary Jordanus Catalani, a French Dominican missionary and explorer. We have no idea when Jordanus Catalani was born, although we know where—in Séverac, in the vicinity of Toulouse. But since he left on his first trip to the East in 1302 he must have been around twenty years old by that time. In 1328 he was made a bishop and nominated to the see of Columbum in 1330. He must have written his book

---

[2] More about "Sir John de Mandeville" and his famous travel book can be found in my book *The Lungfish, the Dodo, and the Unicorn*, Chapter 5, "The Vegetable Animals."

at about that time. In it he spoke of a tree growing in the Spice Islands (the Moluccas) that is virulently poisonous, and especially so when in bloom. At that time one must not approach the tree or one will surely die.

Even though the number of travelers to the Far East increased as time went on, no good description of the poison tree reached Europe. The Europeans were well aware of the fact that the arrows and other weapons of the Javanese and the inhabitants of the other Sunda Islands were often poisoned and that the poison often proved to be very effective. The natives, on the other hand, stated freely that the poison came from a tree, or, more generally, a plant. But they seem to have been silent about which plant or which tree. And if a traveler by chance caught sight of the tree which does produce the poison he did not realize that it was the source. It happens to be a beautiful tall tree with a whitish bark and very "normal"-looking foliage, without any vestige of the threatening appearance the white men indubitably expected. For centuries the reports about the tree were meager, adding various conjectures but no facts.

In the seventeenth century the English, who had meanwhile developed some interest in that area of the globe, decided that it must be possible to find out and they published suggestions that British and other travelers to the Far East pay special attention to the mystery of the poison tree. Any definite information would be gratefully received. One such call for investigation appeared in the *Philosophical Transactions* for 1666 and another was included in the *Enquiries for East India.*

But the first two reports which did bring some new knowledge—although it was mostly Far Eastern folklore—did not originate with English travelers. In fact, it is doubtful whether the two men who did contribute even knew about the English appeals. One of them was the German physician Engelbert Kämpfer, who lived from 1651 to 1716 and who spent much time in Japan and Siam and also on the Sunda

Islands. He is considered one of the first modern explorers of the Far East, and his *History of Japan and Siam* was printed repeatedly in England, for the first time in 1728. Dr. Kämpfer might have spent even more time in the East if he had succeeded in finding employment with the Dutch East India Company, as he had hoped. Since he did not, his stay in the Sunda Sea area was comparatively short. The other man was also born in Germany—in 1627—but probably of Dutch parentage. He did find employment with the Dutch East India Company, spent many years of his life on the island of Amboina, where the Company had its headquarters, and was what was dubbed "Senior Merchant"—actually the staff scientist. His name, in the Latinized version which he employed, was Georgius Everhardus Rumphius. Since Rumphius occupies a good portion of Chapter 8, nothing more need to be told about him here.

Dr. Engelbert Kämpfer's information about the poison tree is not contained in his *History of Japan* but in his other book, the only one that saw print during his lifetime, that is, in 1712. A copy of the original edition is now one of the great rarities on the antiquarian book market. Its title was *Amoenitates exoticae,* which is hard to translate, the meaning being, roughly, "amusing exotic things." The chapter which begins on page 573 is devoted to Asiatic poisons of all kinds; the poison tree is just one item. Kämpfer explained that poisons came from various plants, some of them trees, but that the "true poison tree" grows only on Macassar, a name then used for the whole island of Celebes.

This tree can be reached, Kämpfer continued, only under extreme danger of life, "for you have to enter areas of the jungle which abound with wild carnivores." The collector of the poison is usually a criminal who takes with him a piece of well-aged hard bamboo, sharpened at one end. He approaches the tree with the wind, thrusts the bamboo into its bark, and waits until it has filled up with sap "to the next knot." He then pours the sap into an earthen vessel he carries with him for this purpose, leaves the jungle as fast as he can, and brings the vessel to his king, thereby assuring himself an automatic pardon for whatever crime he may have committed. "This," Kämpfer concluded, "is what the natives of Celebes told me, but who can expect unembellished truth from the mouth of an Asiatic? Certain is that the king of Macassar and the other nobles anoint their daggers and weapons with a deadly poison, but it loses in potency with time."

The other reporter, Rumphius, had much more to say, and in a way something far more definite, because he had obtained a twig and a fruit of the poison tree, both of which he pictured. These pictures appear in his *Herbarium amboinense*, published at Amsterdam in 1741, almost four decades after its author's death. The book consists of seven volumes in largest folio, printed in two columns. The left-hand column is in Latin, the right-hand column in Dutch. The Dutch title for the book is *Het Amboinsche Kruid-Boek*, both titles meaning, of course, "Book of the Plants of Amboina." The chapter on the poison tree is Chapter 45 in Book iii, volume ii. The Latin column is headed *"Arbor Toxicaria, Ipo,"* the Dutch column *"Macassarsche Gift-Boom."*[3]

At no point does Rumphius claim to have seen the tree; all he had seen was that single twig. But he had been told that there were poison trees of different strengths and he assumed that they were male and female trees, the poison of the female being weaker by far. The native method of obtaining the sap is described just as it is in Kämpfer's book (but without involving condemned criminals): the man jabs a sharpened piece of bamboo into the trunk and waits for it to fill up with the sap, which Rumphius calls "bloody."

The poison is so much stronger in the male tree that one

[3] This happens to be an especially misleading combination of words for an English-speaking person, since both words look familiar. But in Dutch, as in German, *Gift* means "poison," while the Dutch word *Boom* (in German *Baum*) means "tree."

cannot approach it without having covered all exposed parts
of the body with fabric. And because of the poison nothing
grows under the tree, so that the soil is bare. "Under the
most powerful kind you are supposed to find another sign,
namely dead birds which tried to rest in the boughs of the
tree, lost consciousness and dropped to the ground, dead."
Rumphius tells in detail how the sap is treated; I am not
quite sure whether he is still reporting tales of the natives or
whether he actually watched the operation. He concludes
the account with a bit of native folklore: when a good quantity of poison has been removed from a tree it is felled,
because the natives believe that then all the people who are
struck by weapons smeared with this sap will die too. If they
left the tree alive the poison would slowly weaken and the
weapons would be less deadly. The sentence Rumphius uses
to conclude this paragraph is typical of the man: *"Doch ik
geloove, datze dit met de weinigste boomen doen, ander-
zonden die al lang vermindert syn."* ("But I believe that they
do that to only a very few trees, otherwise they would have
become rare long ago.")

In the normal course of events later travelers would have
visited the trees themselves, observed the process of tapping,
and in time produced botanical descriptions of the tree and
chemical analyses of the poison. Eventually all this did happen, but there was a fantastic interlude.

Sometime during 1783 the editor of the *London Magazine*
received a manuscript on the poison tree. It came to him
from a Mr. Heydinger, whom the editor of the magazine
identified in print as the former owner of a German book-
store in London. According to Mr. Heydinger, he was not
the author of the manuscript, but had merely translated it
into English from Dutch; the author was a Dutchman named
N. P. Foersch. It was stated in the article itself that Mr.
Foersch had been (and presumably still was) in the services
of the Dutch East India Company; in 1774-76 he had been

stationed at Batavia as a surgeon, and the information contained in the article had been collected at that time.

Since Mr. Heydinger can be traced to some extent—you can't very well run a bookshop and stay anonymous—but Mr. N. P. Foersch remains absolutely untraceable, one might toy with the idea that the manuscript submitted to the editor of the *London Magazine* was not a translation from the Dutch at all and that N. P. Foersch was one of the more successful inventions of Mr. Heydinger. The wording of the short editorial which introduces the article seems to hint ever so gently at this possibility. And it begins with the sentence: "This account, we must allow, appears so *marvellous,* that even the Credulous might be staggered." The editor obviously washed his hands but could not get himself to pass up the opportunity of printing the article. It appeared in the December issue for 1783, beginning on page 511. The main assertions of the piece were that the terrible tree, called Bohun-Upas, grew 27 leagues from Batavia in the interior of Java and that nobody could live within a radius of 12 to 14 miles of it. Naturally under these circumstances Mr. Foersch had not seen the tree himself, but he had spoken to many people who knew all about it and he had even succeeded in obtaining two leaves.

The astonishing report, about which more later, was reprinted as fast as physically possible—*translated from the English* of the *London Magazine*—in the Dutch *Allgemeene Vaderlandsche Letteroefeningen* in 1784. French and German magazines also published translations, some using the Dutch translation as their raw material. Naturally other publications in England and in Holland reprinted the stuff too, or at least published excerpts. Still, the story might have been forgotten again if Dr. Erasmus Darwin had not used it in his *Loves of the Plants.*

Erasmus Darwin's contribution to the lore of the upas tree ran as follows:

Where seas of glass with gay reflections smile
Round the green coasts of Java's palmy isle,
A spacious plain extends its upland scene,
Rocks rise on rocks, and fountains gush between;
Soft zephyrs blow, eternal summers reign,
And showers prolific bless the soil,—in vain!
—No spicy nutmeg scents the vernal gales,
Nor towering plantain shades the mid-day vales;
No grassy mantle hides the sable hills,
No flowery chaplet crowns the trickling rills;
Nor tufted moss, nor leathery lichen creeps
In russet tapestry on the crumbling steeps.
—No step retreating, on the sand impress'd
Invites the visit of a second guest;
No refluent fin the unpeopled stream divides,
No revolant pinion cleaves the airy tides;
Nor handed moles, nor beaked worms return
That mining pass the irremeable bourn.—
Fierce in dread silence on the blasted heath
Fell Upas sits, the Hydra-Tree of death.
Lo, from one root, the envenom'd soil below
A thousand vegetative serpents grow;
In shining rays the scaly monster spreads
O'er ten square leagues his far-diverging heads;
Or in one trunk entwists his tangled form,
Looks o'er the clouds, and hisses in the storm
Steep'd in fell poison, as his sharp teeth part,
A thousand tongues in quick vibration dart;
Snatch the proud eagle towering over the heath,
Or pounce the lion, as he stalks beneath;
Or strew, as marshall'd hosts contend in vain,
With human skeletons the whitened plain.

After a little pause to regain his breath the reader no
doubt looked for and found the "philosophical note" which
justified these lines. It read:

There is a poison-tree in the island of Java, which is said by
its effluvia to have depopulated the country for 12 or 14 miles
round the place of its growth. It is called, in the Malayan lan-

guage, Bohun-Upas; with the juice of it the most poisonous
arrows are prepared; and, to gain this, the condemned criminals
are sent to the tree with proper direction both to get the juice
and to secure themselves from the malignant exhalations of the
tree; and are pardoned if they bring back a certain quantity of
the poison. But by the registers there kept, not one in four are
said to return. Not only animals of all kinds, both quadrupeds,
fish and birds, but all kinds of vegetables are also destroyed by
the effluvia of the noxious tree; so that, in a district of 12 or 14
miles around it, the face of the earth is quite barren and rocky,
intermitted only with the skeletons of men and animals, affording
a scene of melancholy beyond that what poets have described
or painters delineated. Two younger trees of its own species are
said to grow near it.

The remaining sentence of this note, following after the
"near it" will strike a modern reader as almost as bad as the
story itself. It reads: "See *London Magazine* for 1784 or
1783." Sometime later Dr. Darwin must have found his reference because at the very end of the book the article from
the *London Magazine* is reprinted in its entirety, with the
exception of one paragraph which is said to be in Malayan.
The "philosophical note" summarizes Mr. Foersch's article
pretty well, but there are a number of alleged facts which
Erasmus Darwin left out. The condemned criminals which
are to gather poison from the tree are provided with leather
caps with glasses, and leather gloves, and usually assemble in
the house of a priest just outside the danger area. They are
given a silver or tortoise-shell box which they have to fill.
The priest told the Dutch surgeon that he kept book on the
criminals, who were often accompanied by their families to
his house. In thirty years he saw seven hundred criminals
try for their pardon, of which seventy returned. When the
man sets out he is instructed "to go to the tree before the
wind; to go as fast as possible all the way; and to return
against the wind." Either from the priest, or from a pardoned criminal who was successful, Mr. Foersch obtained

two leaves which had fallen off the tree. He learned that the tree stood near a rivulet and was only of middling size, with five or six young trees of the same kind growing nearby from a ground covered with dead bodies.

When the priest was asked why God permitted such a monstrous growth, he replied—this is the paragraph which is given both in Malayan and in English in the first publication —that their holy book told them that more than a hundred years earlier the area was inhabited by a tribe strongly addicted to the sins of Sodom and Gomorrah, that Mohammed, after many years of patience, finally applied to God, and God caused the tree to grow which destroyed them all. Later a group of rebels, referred to as the Moo-rebels, fled into the area and started building their huts, knowing that nobody would follow them. Two months later all but two hundred were dead.

Mr. Foersch reasoned that one of the main aspects of the danger caused by the tree was that it grew in an area where there was never a good wind; thus the poison could accumulate. If it were windy there, he reasoned, the poison would be dispersed and only the immediate vicinity of the tree would be dangerous. While he, for obvious reasons, had not seen the tree itself, he had been an eye-witness of something almost as interesting. In 1776 it was found out that thirteen (always an unlucky number) of the Sultan's concubines had been unfaithful and they were sentenced to death. They were undressed to the navel and tied to posts. Then the executioner lanced each of the women between the breasts with a small poisoned knife. Five minutes after the lancing they all showed severe tremors and another eleven minutes later they were all dead. Mr. Foersch then secured a poisoned blade himself and tried it on three or four stray dogs, all of which died within minutes. He remarked further that "on the Macassar coast" there grew a tree called Cajoe-Upas in fair numbers, bearing "poison of the same type, but not half so violent and malignant as that of the tree of Java."

The Dutch, being closest to the scene, were the first to take action. When a copy of the issue of the *Letteroefeningen* containing the translation of Foersch's article finally arrived in Java, a local society, the *Bataviaasch Genootschap,* dispatched an ambassadorial party to the ruler, Sultan Pakoe Boewono III, asking him whether there was such a tree a comparatively short distance from Batavia or anywhere else on the island, and whether he used its poison in the reported manner to dispatch convicted criminals. The Sultan replied that he did not have the pleasure of having such a marvelous tree growing in his domain and, as far as the other question was concerned, he had a sufficient number of effective means. The Dutch were satisfied with that answer and in 1789 the *Letteroefeningen* carried a note that the *Oepas-Boom*[4] was a fable. Of course, it was added, there was a tree which produced a poison juice for arrows, but the poison could be collected easily, and nobody had ever found a dead bird which had died because it had been sitting on such a tree.

In Europe they did not quite know what to think. The issue of the Dutch magazine (not of very large circulation) which debunked the story appeared in precisely the same year that Erasmus Darwin wrote his poem. When the poem was published three years later, the appended reprint of the article by Foersch seemed to support the latter. Darwin had even appended another reprint, excerpts from a dissertation by one Johannes Aejmelaeus, prepared under the supervision of the then very famous Swedish botanist Professor Carl Peter Thunberg, a direct pupil of Linnaeus and the successor to his chair at the University of Uppsala. Aejmelaeus apparently took his cues from Rumphius: You can get near the tree if you are completely wrapped up in linen. Even then only the dried sap can be collected; if fresh sap is wanted the tree must be tapped by means of a very long

---

[4] In Dutch "oe" is pronounced "oo." The word "upas" (pronounced "oopas") is simply the Malay word for a vegetable poison, while an animal poison (such as that of a snake) is called *bisa* and a mineral poison *ratchoon.*

bamboo pole. They try to tap close to the root because the
poison is more potent there. Aejmelaeus added, probably
paraphrasing Kämpfer, that "the poison loses much of its
power in the time of one year and in a few years becomes
totally harmless."

In France Monsieur Pierre Joseph Buch'oz, who had
written little treatises with titles like *Dissertation sur le café*
and *Dissertation sur le cacao* (yes, tea too!), deserted his
theme of pleasant drinks for a discussion of the arrow poison
of the Ipo tree. And a German, E. W. Martius, used the
treatises by Aejmelaeus and Buch'oz to acquaint his com-
patriots with the marvels of the Sunda Island poison trees.[5]

While *Loves of the Plants* was still selling briskly, the
first completely sober and virtually complete description of
the tree was being written. Its author was the French naturalist L. Th. Leschenault de la Tour, who had traveled in eastern Java in 1804. After his return the *Annales du Muséum
d'Histoire Naturelle* printed his story. It was a perfectly
simple one. It had been no problem to have the tree identified by the natives; you only had to go where it grew,
which was not at the seashore. "*Antiaris* is very large,"
Leschenault wrote. "I have always found it in fertile places
and, owing to such fertility, surrounded by dense vegetation
which is in no way harmed by its proximity." He had tapped
the tree and had carried "a large quantity" of the poison
back to France with him, without poisoning the whole ship
or even himself. He had tested the poison on rabbits and
chickens and had even made, inadvertently, an experiment
with human beings:

> The tree which furnished the specimens of the plant itself and
> the poison which I brought back with me was more than 100
> feet tall and the trunk, at its base, was about 18 feet in circum-

[5] The titles of these treatises are: *Dissertatio de arbore toxicaria Macas-
sariense,* Uppsala, 1788 (Aejmelaeus); *Dissertation sur l'Ipo, espèce de poison
subtil, dont se servent les sauvages empoisonner leur flèches,* Paris, 1790
(Buch'oz); *Gesammelte Nachrichten über den Makassarischen Giftbaum,* Er-
langen, 1792 (Martius).

ference. A Javanese whom I had hired to get me some branches of the tree while it was in flower climbed up to cut them. He had scarcely climbed 25 feet when he found himself so sick that he had to come down. He was ill for several days with vertigo and nausea and vomited repeatedly. Another Javanese went to the very top of the tree and cut flowering branches for me; he was not affected at all. Later, I had a tree measuring about 4 feet around the trunk felled for me and I walked into the midst of the broken branches, getting face and hands smeared with the gum that oozed from the breaks. True, I took the precaution of washing myself at once. . . . I have seen lizards and insects on its trunk and birds perching on its boughs.

This sober report was followed by a lecture on the effects of the poison by B. C. Brodie, Esq., F.R.S., "read to the Royal Society 21st February 1811" and printed in *Philosophical Transactions,* Part 1 of 1811, stating that the poison acts by paralyzing the heart. In 1814 there followed another perfectly sober and fine report by Thomas Horsfield, entitled *Essay on the Oepas* and published by the *Genootschap* in Batavia.

Did this kill the legend created by Foersch or Heydinger and publicized by Erasmus Darwin?

Well, yes and no. In works of information the story was sharply debunked. But Darwin's poem, with all the appendixes, was still being reprinted. And poets just would not abandon the wonderful idea. In 1820 or thereabouts (the book has no date so one has to judge by its typography) a play with the title *The Law of Java; or, The Poison Tree* was printed in London. In the unlikely case that anyone should come across a copy I hereby issue fair warning.

It was much more important that, as late as 1828, the theme was again adopted by one of the great poets, namely Alexander Sergeevitch Pushkin. His poem is called *Antchár*; in Russian the name upas, which heads translations, would sound silly—there is no proper word "upas" in Russian but it suggests an exceedingly ungrammatical way of saying that somebody pastured something, which is obviously not in keeping with the grim theme. And grim the poem is: "On the wan and arid desert, in soil baked red hot, the antchár stands like a grim watcher." It goes on to say that it is unique in all the universe—the standard translation has "isolated" instead of the correct "unique," because the translator had to

Pushkin's "Antchár tree," as it might have been pictured (but wasn't) at the time the poem was written

make it rhyme—and "the Nature of the thirsting plain bore it on a day of wrath." The poem is factually wrong on every count but most impressively stated, so impressively that succeeding generations of millions of Russians knew it by heart and presumably believed it.

After Foersch and Pushkin the scientific truth about "dread upas" is necessarily anticlimactic. The only amusement one can get out of the facts is to see how they compare with the wild stories of nearly two centuries ago. The scientific name, given by Leschenault, is *Antiaris toxicaria,* and botanical handbooks say calmly that it is a very tall tree which can easily reach 150 feet; that its wood is white, spongy, and light; that the sap is sticky and thick, white when the tree is young and yellowish when it is old, and hardens quickly, turning brown in the process. "Leaves are short-stemmed, oval-shaped, and sometimes serrated and asymmetrical, upper side shiny and almost smooth with few short hairs, underside with more hairs and rough to the touch. Leaves of young trees tend to be smoother than those of old. Male flowers clustered, female flowers single. Fruit is red, containing one hard-shelled seed, fruit flesh very attractive to birds and edible!" Then the handbooks proclaim with the air of a landscape description that "in the more elevated areas of the Javanese rain forest the poisonous upas trees tower high over the luxuriant underbrush." Pushkin notwithstanding, the upas tree needs lots of moisture to thrive.

Far from being in any way unique, the upas tree has quite a number of relatives. The nearest is *Antiaris innoxia,* which is more numerous and not poisonous at all. Others, some mildly poisonous, some innocuous, are *Antiaris dubia* and *Antiaris rufa.* And a tree originally named *Lepuranda saccadora* should be called by its revised name of *Antiaris saceidora.* All of them are members of the fig family.

Only when it comes to the poison itself is there some slight resemblance between fact and fiction. The sap *is* poisonous and will kill a large animal within minutes, even if it did not strike a vulnerable spot. It has also been found to be true that sap taken from a tap close to the ground is more toxic than that from a tap ten feet high on the trunk. After a first chemical analysis in 1824 which somehow miscarried, the chemist G. J. Mulder succeeded in 1837 in isolating the poison, which he named antiarin. It forms 6/10 of 1 per cent of the weight of fresh sap and 1.7 per cent of the weight of dried sap. The pure poison is crystalline; the crystals melt at 440 degrees Fahrenheit. The chemical formula was given by Mulder as $C_{27}H_{42}O_{10}$.

So much for detail about the tree which cannot be approached.

The "arrow-poison tree" of Java, *Antiaris toxicaria*, the terrible upas tree of legend

If any date can be given at all it would be safe to say that the botanical legend of the terrible tree had been laid to rest by 1837, when scientific journals had published such detail as has just been quoted. But in just that year another side avenue in the story of the upas tree was opened, one which suggests that "Mr. Foersch," though indubitably a liar of the first magnitude, may have been aided by some rumors he heard in Java—provided he ever actually was there.

In that year the *Journal of the Royal Asiatic Society* published a lecture by one Lieutenant Colonel W. H. Sykes, F.R.S., with the title "Remarks on the Origin of the Popular Belief in the Upas or Poison Tree of Java." Some of the features of the fantastic tale, Lieutenant Colonel Sykes said, may have been due to a simple misunderstanding. Java is an island full of active or only very slightly dormant volcanoes. One of the most common by-products of volcanism is carbon dioxide, a gas which, as is well known, is odorless, invisible, and heavier than air. Unless dispersed by wind carbon dioxide can and will accumulate in depressions very much as water does. While carbon dioxide is certainly not poisonous but completely harmless to animals and people, and even beneficial to vegetation, a high accumulation of carbon dioxide can be dangerous simply because it displaces the oxygen. In such a case death can occur from what might be called "drowning" in carbon dioxide. A famous and long-known example of such a situation is the Grotta del Cane ("dog cave") in Italy, about halfway between Naples and Pozzuoli. A carbon-dioxide well situated inside this cave causes an almost pure layer of the gas to cover the bottom of the cave to a height of, say, 2 feet. There is no danger at all to people, because the air above that layer is perfectly breathable. But a small animal, such as a dog, which enters the cave, cannot reach above the carbon-dioxide layer and dies quickly of suffocation.

The same phenomenon can very easily occur on an island as highly volcanic as Java happens to be. Lieutenant Colonel Sykes stated that there actually was something like the Grotta del Cane on Java, but much larger in extent. He reported that the botanist Horsfield—himself one of the debunkers of the upas tree legend—had heard about a "poisonous valley" from the natives but did not visit it himself since the natives refused to guide him. But Colonel Sykes had received a letter from a Mr. Loudon, a land-owner on Java, who claimed to have seen the "poisonous valley" which the Javanese called Guwo-Upas. It was located some three miles from a place called Batur.[6] After some discussion Mr. Loudon and several other Englishmen residing in the vicinity made up a small party to explore Guwo-Upas. The story of the trip—which took place on July 4, 1830—describes what was very obviously a climb up an extinct volcano and into its crater, although Mr. Loudon did not say so himself. He wrote that the poisonous valley was roughly circular, with a diameter estimated at 300 yards. Vegetation extended downward into the valley almost to the bottom, and the party, somewhat awed by skeletons of animals of various kinds and even of men, which they saw below them, descended as far as they dared. They carried two dogs and several chickens with them. The birds —presumably with their wings tied—were dropped below the vegetation line at a convenient spot. They seemed to be dead a minute and a half later. Then one of the dogs was dropped. It made a few convulsive movements at first and then seemed to settle down to sleep; the observers could see it breathing deeply. The other dog ran down and then behaved very much like the first. The observers estimated that one dog lived for 7 minutes and the other for 18. The figures are estimates because they could not be certain of the moment of death and they did not dare, for obvious reasons, to go lower themselves.

Offhand, this makes a rather attractive explanation. That carbon dioxide will issue from fissures in the floor of a dead volcano is a well-known occurrence. The ringwall of the crater itself, acting as a windbreak, will permit the gas to build up to a high concentration. And animals which some-how get in would surely suffocate, especially since the inner wall of the crater may be difficult to climb. And if such a

[6] I did not find such a place name on any of the maps I consulted.

spectacle is seen by somebody who doesn't even know that carbon dioxide exists and is reported to somebody else who also has no inkling of the true cause, all kinds of stories will originate.

I have not been able to find further mention of this particular poison valley in more recent literature. It may well be that it does not exist any more: if carbon dioxide stopped issuing—in other words, if the steady supply was interrupted —such an open-air valley would clear up rather fast. But I did find a few statements about similar phenomena on Java, on a much smaller scale, to be sure. Since, in any volcanic area, there can be places where animals suddenly collapse and die from no discernible cause, carbon dioxide may well have contributed its share to the story of the Tree of Death which is so poisonous that it cannot even be approached.

7: The Man-Eating Tree
of Madagascar

MADAGASCAR—228,000 square miles in extent—is one of the world's largest islands, ranking fourth in size after Greenland, New Guinea, and Borneo. Though now separated from Africa by the 250-mile-wide Mozambique Channel, it once obviously was a part of the African continent. Whether the land which once formed the connection is now at the bottom of the Mozambique Channel, or whether the two land masses literally drifted apart like a smaller ice floe splitting off from a bigger one, is still an undecided question. But no matter how the separation took place it must have been accompanied by considerable violence. Ancient volcanoes are numerous on Madagascar, especially in its eastern portion; warm springs still abound; and in the region of the Ankàratra mountains a full 2000 square miles are covered by ancient lava.

Madagascar is also quite unbelievable as regards its native fauna. Through the soft soil of its tropical forests crawl earthworms a full yard long and about an inch in thickness. One of their enemies is the tanrek, a small animal resembling (and related to) the European hedgehog. The tanrek, unassuming as it is in appearance, has relatively the largest mouth of any mammal, maybe because of those enormous earthworms, and absolutely the largest litters of any mammal, twenty young being about the rule—presumably because the tanrek has enemies in turn which like to eat it. Big mouth, large litters, and all, the tanrek's ancestry goes back in a straight and unbroken line to a tribe of ancient mammals which began to inhabit the earth at a time when the last of the dinosaurs were still around. Not quite so ancient but still old enough is another of Madagascar's wonder animals, the fossa or *Kryptoprokta,* a catlike animal of about the size of a fox, with a very long tail and elongated limbs. Harmless to man—in spite of some wild stories to the contrary—the fossa represents an otherwise extinct group of ancient catlike mammals, one which evolved in the obvious direction of the modern cats without quite becoming cats.

But the characteristic animals of Madagascar are the lemurs, which may be said to bear about the same relationship to the monkeys as the fossa does to the cats. The vast majority of all the still living species of lemurs inhabit the trees of Madagascar, hunting insects and calling to one another with plaintive wails. Since they are all night prowlers they are rarely to be seen in zoological gardens, even if the garden has some theoretically on exhibit. In size they range from that of a small rat to that of a large cat. Weirdest of them is no doubt the aye-aye—the name itself is weird enough. It gives the impression of a cat with many monkey traits, or a catlike monkey; its large protruding ears are built to catch the faintest sound made by unsuspecting insects, and one of its fingers is more than twice as long as the others, as skinny as a living limb can be and equipped with a curved hooklike nail for dragging insects out from under the bark of trees.

Though Madagascar's still-living indigenous animals are quite small—the only exception being a fairly large crocodile —this is a comparatively recent development. If a shipload of Crusaders—it was at about the time of the Crusades that Malay sailors reached the island and began to settle it—had been blown to Madagascar in some manner they would have found some spectacular additions to the present-day fauna.

There were two or three species of hippopotamus, about two-thirds the size of the well-known African kind; there were a small zebu, a gigantic land tortoise, and a full dozen species of ostrich-like flightless birds, *Aepyornis,* the tallest of them, towering high over any living ostrich. And there was *Megalodapis,* a lemur the size of a man, which, because of its size and weight, must have lived on the ground and quite possibly moved through the night walking on its hind legs only.[1]

The flora of Madagascar is almost as strange as its fauna. The famous "Traveler's Tree," *Urania speciosa* of the botanists, displays a flat fan of enormous palm leaves on top of a tall trunk. This 100-foot-tall palm has its common name because clear water collects in reservoirs near the trunk and can be tapped without harming the tree. To the natives it provides much more than water. The trunk is timber. The outer covering of the trunk, after a thorough beating with wooden mallets to soften it, serves as a carpet. The fronds thatch the house, and even the individual leaves are used: they are twisted into spoons. Other typical Madagascar flora are the beefwood tree (*Casuarina equisitifolia*), a tall firlike tree, several species of screw pine (*Pandanus*), and the large "Madagascar spice" tree (*Ravintsara madagascariensis*), which bears fragrant fruit and has equally fragrant leaves and bark. There is a relative of the castor-oil plant with seeds which are so oily that they can simply be strung on a reed like beads and ignited to burn slowly like a candle. Quite obviously, this has been called the candle-nut tree. And there is the raphia palm, *Sagus ruffia,* with enormous fronds that have a tough fibrous midrib which can serve as a rope without much treatment and, if treated, provide fibers for weaving. Since the frond of this palm, when dried, looks like an enormous bird feather, it was at least once—but probably more than

---

[1] Our first literary sources about the existence of Madagascar are Arabic in origin, and I have occasionally wondered whether *Megalodapis* might not be the "prototype" of the djinns and afrits of the *Arabian Nights.*

just once—sent to a curious inquirer as a feather from Sind-
bad's fabulous roc, which was believed to nest in Madagascar.

One would think that all this should provide enough
scientific fame for any island, even one 228,000 square miles
in extent. But to many people Madagascar is also known as
the home of one more natural marvel: the man-eating tree.

There are, as everyone knows, plants which catch and
digest insects, usually plants which grow on poor soil and
which are able to survive on such soil mostly because they
have evolved methods of deriving an extra income from
unwary insects. Their methods differ. The sun-dew *Drosera*
has small "tentacles"—more precisely, stalked glands—growing over the upper surfaces of its leaves. If a fly alights on a
leaf it will stick to the mucilage drops at the ends of the
tentacles it happens to touch. Other tentacles reach over
leisurely and the whole leaf slowly closes over the victim.
The method of catching insects is actually the flypaper
method, *if* flypaper curled itself around the fly after catching
it and digested it to make more mucilage. The Venus' fly
trap *Dionaea,* on the other hand, actually operates a trap,
similar to the steel traps used when wolves put in an un-
wanted appearance. The two lobes of the leaf can close over
an insect, and moreover the edges of the leaf lobes have a
number of spikes which interlock. The digestive glands are
on the leaf itself, as are three sensitive hairs on each leaf
lobe which actuate the mechanism. In cold weather an insect
may get away in time; when it is warm the speed of the leaf's
movement is fast enough to trap anything that cannot break
out by brute strength. If Dionaea uses a wolf or bear trap,
the aquatic bladderwort *Utricularia* evolved a kind of mouse-
trap—tiny bladders sprouting from submerged shoots which
are equipped with a valve that opens inward and in a most
ingenious manner even applies a push to the victim. The
fourth major method is that of the pitcher plant (*Nepenthes*
and others) which has, sprouting from the leaf tips, regular
pitchers half filled with weak digestive juice. The half-open

lid of the pitcher does not close, as has occasionally been stated; it merely has the purpose of keeping rain out.[2]

All these plants are quite small and their victims are tiny, flies and small grasshopper larvae, mosquito larvae in the case of *Utricularia* (using this plant for mosquito control has been suggested), and an occasional tiny freshwater crustacean. A very young tree frog might happen to get into the pitcher of one of the larger varieties of pitcher plants once in a while, but on the whole these plants are what Charles Darwin called them: insectivorous.

But rumor, persistently peddled in Sunday supplements of the more lurid type and in small articles in various odd little magazines, insisted that somewhere, in the interior of distant islands, Nature had applied the principle of the Venus' fly trap on a large scale. It was either on Mindanao in the Philippine Islands or in the interior of Madagascar. In one version the natives shunned the tree which might catch them; in another they appeased it with regular sacrifices, which, of course, had to be kept from the eyes of the White Man. (The optimum solution was, of course, to feed the White Man to the tree to keep the tale from spreading and the tree satisfied.)

The story of the man-eating tree of Madagascar was alleged to have been started with a letter written from Madagascar in 1878 by an eye-witness of the native ceremony of sacrifice. The name of the eye-witness is given as Carl Liche, the name of the recipient of the letter as Dr. Omelius Fredlowski, a Polish scientist. This letter was printed "in full" in a book called *Madagascar, Land of the Man-Eating Tree,* by Chase Salmon Osborn, LL.D., published in New York in 1924. Since the book had only a small circulation and has been out of print for decades, I'll give the text of the letter here:

The Mkodos, of Madagascar, are a very primitive race, going entirely naked, having only faint vestiges of tribal relations, and

[2] The classical work on these plants is Charles Darwin's *Insectivorous Plants* (2d ed., 1875); the most comprehensive is Francis Ernest Lloyd's *The Carnivorous Plants* (Chronica Botanica, 1942), which also lists all the earlier literature.

no religion beyond that of the awful reverence which they pay to the sacred tree. They dwell entirely in caves hollowed out of the limestone rocks in their hills, and are one of the smallest races, the men seldom exceeding fifty-six inches in height. At the bottom of a valley (I had no barometer, but should not think it over four hundred feet above the level of the sea), and near its eastern extremity, we came to a deep tarn-like lake about a mile in diameter, the sluggish oily water of which overflowed into a tortuous reedy canal that went unwillingly into the recesses of a black forest composed of jungle below and palms above. A path diverging from its southern side struck boldly for the heart of the forbidding and seemingly impenetrable forest. Hendrick led the way along this path, I following closely, and behind me a curious rabble of Mkodos, men, women and children. Suddenly all the natives began to cry "Tepe! Tepe!" and Hendrick, stopping short, said, "Look!" The sluggish canal-like stream here wound slowly by, and in a bare spot in its bend was the most singular of trees. I have called it "Crinoida," because when its leaves are in action it bears a striking resemblance to that well-known fossil the crinoid lily-stone or St. Cuthbert's head. It was now at rest, however, and I will try to describe it to you. If you can imagine a pineapple eight feet high and thick in proportion resting upon its base and denuded of leaves, you will have a good idea of the trunk of the tree, which, however, was not the color of an anana, but a dark dingy brown, and apparently as hard as iron. From the apex of this truncated cone (at least two feet in diameter) eight leaves hung sheer to the ground, like doors swung back on their hinges. These leaves, which were joined at the top of the tree at regular intervals, were about eleven or twelve feet long, and shaped very much like the leaves of the American agave or century plant. They were two feet through at their thickest point and three feet wide, tapering to a sharp point that looked like a cow's horn, very convex on the outer (but now under surface), and on the under (now upper) surface slightly concave. This concave face was thickly set with strong thorny hooks like those on the head of the teazle. These leaves hanging thus limp and lifeless, dead green in color, had in appearance the massive strength of oak fibre. The apex of the cone was a round white concave figure like a smaller plate set within a larger one. This was not a flower but a receptacle, and there exuded into it a clear treacly liquid, honey sweet, and possessed of violent intoxicating and soporific properties. From underneath the rim (so to speak) of the undermost plate a series of long hairy green tendrils stretched out in every direction towards the horizon. These were seven or eight feet long, and tapered from four inches to a half inch in diameter, yet they stretched out stiffly as iron rods. Above these (from between the upper and under cup) six white almost transparent palpi reared themselves towards the sky, twirling and twisting with a marvelous incessant motion, yet constantly reaching upwards. Thin as reeds and frail as quills, apparently they were yet five or six feet tall, and were so constantly and vigorously in motion, with such a subtle, sinuous, silent throbbing against the air, that they made me shudder in spite of myself, with their suggestion of serpents flayed, yet dancing upon their tails. The description I am giving you now is partly made up from a subsequent careful inspection of the plant. My observations on this occasion were suddenly interrupted by the natives, who had been shrieking around the tree with their shrill voices, and chanting what Hendrick told me were propitiatory hymns to the great tree devil. With still wilder shrieks and chants they now surrounded one of the women, and urged her with the points of their javelins, until slowly, and with despairing face, she climbed up the stalk of the tree and stood on the summit of the cone, the palpi swirling all about her. "Tsik! Tsik!" ("Drink, drink!") cried the men. Stooping, she drank of the viscid fluid in the cup, rising instantly again, with wild frenzy in her face and convulsive cords in her limbs. But she did not jump down, as she seemed to intend to do. Oh, no! The atrocious cannibal tree that had been so inert and dead came to sudden savage life. The slender delicate palpi, with the fury of starved serpents, quivered a moment over her head, then as if instinct with demoniac intelligence fastened upon her in sudden coils round and round her neck and arms; then while her awful screams and yet more awful laughter rose wildly to be instantly strangled down again into a gurgling moan, the tendrils one after another, like green serpents, with brutal energy and infernal rapidity, rose, retracted themselves, and wrapped her about in fold after fold, ever tightening with cruel swiftness and the savage tenacity of anacondas fastening upon their prey. It was the barbarity of the Laocoön without its beauty—this strange horrible murder. And now the great leaves slowly rose and stiffly, like the arms of a derrick, erected themselves in the air, approached one another and closed about the dead and hampered victim with the silent force of a hydraulic press and the ruthless purpose of a thumb screw. A moment more, and while I could see the bases of these great levers pressing more tightly towards each other, from their interstices there trickled down the stalk of the tree great streams of the viscid honey-like fluid mingled horribly with the blood and oozing viscera of the victim. At sight of this the savage hordes around me, yelling madly, bounded forward, crowded to the tree, clasped it, and with cups, leaves, hands and tongues each one obtained enough of the liquor to send him mad and frantic. Then ensued a grotesque and indescribably hideous orgy, from which even while its convulsive madness was turning rapidly into delirium and insensibility, Hendrick dragged me hurriedly away into the recesses of the forest, hiding me from the dangerous brutes. May I never see such a sight again.

The retracted leaves of the great tree kept their upright position during ten days, then when I came one morning they were prone again, the tendrils stretched, the palpi floating, and nothing but a white skull at the foot of the tree to remind me of the sacrifice that had taken place there. I climbed into a neighboring tree, and saw that all trace of the victim had disappeared and the cup was again supplied with the viscid fluid.

In his book Chase Salmon Osborn, who claims to have spent much time in Madagascar, declares that he had not seen the tree himself, that he had never met a missionary who did see it, but that they all asserted that "all the tribes" talk about it. Because he could not obtain a newer description he fell back on the old letter, of which he wrote that it is "the most lurid and dramatic description of the man-eating tree of Madagascar I have seen." That might well be granted, but we now come to the question of whether, in addition to being lurid and dramatic, it is also true.

Offhand, I'd say botanists are apt to shake their heads about the mechanism involved. Not that large leaves rising in the manner described are inherently impossible, but the dancing "palpi" would certainly be unique in the plant kingdom. Besides there is the carefully described fact that the tree does not respond until the victim has climbed to the top of the trunk and presumably touched the "palpi." This arrangement would leave the tree in a badly undernourished condition because it would virtually depend on natives feeding it, with or without ceremony. Its only normal nonhuman victims would be tree-climbing animals, which are all quite small. In tropical countries monkeys are the most numerous tree climbers; in Madagascar these would be lemurs. Both monkeys and lemurs would quickly learn to recognize this type of tree and carefully avoid it. Which leaves an occasional bird as the only possible victim.

But let's approach the story from a different angle.

Sophia Prior, in her *Carnivorous Plants and "The Man-eating Tree"* (Botanical Leaflet No. 23 of the Chicago Museum of Natural History, 1939), stated, as many others had, that Carl Liche's letter was first published in the *Carlsruhe Scientific Journal.* This information is copied from C. S. Osborn, who added that the magazine was published by "Graefe and Walther in Karlsruhe." Osborn added further that the letter also was published "in several European scientific publications" and "was first published in America by the *New York World* in 1880."

Copies of newspapers three-quarters of a century old are hard to come by, so I did not check the *World.* But scientific magazines are another story; they are easily accessible in any large library. The first strange fact I turned up was that half a dozen European scientific journals picked at random did not mention the letter. The second strange fact was that the Carlsruhe (or Karlsruhe, which is the more recent spelling) journal was not in any of the libraries I checked. That the files of journals are not complete is, unfortunately, a common occurrence, deplored by both researchers and librarians. That a whole file should be completely missing is rare. But there is always the Library of Congress. No such publication was in its catalogue. Of course, even the Library of Congress doesn't have everything ever printed, but it does have a Union Catalogue Division which knows where everything can be found. But whether you spelled Karlsruhe with a "K" or a "C," and whether the English word "journal" had originally been *Zeitschrift,* or *Berichte,* or *Beiträge,* the Union Catalogue Division had never heard of it. Nor could they find a publishing firm of "Graefe and Walther"; they asked helpfully whether I meant "Graefe and Unzer," but I didn't, for I knew Graefe and Unzer well, and it was located in Königsberg, East Prussia, and not in Karlsruhe.

Then I started checking—or tried to—on Mr. Liche and Dr. Fredlowski. They might be listed in Webster's Biographical Dictionary, but they weren't. At least one of them should be somewhere in the Encyclopaedia Britannica, but wasn't. Since both were Europeans it seemed likely that they might be mentioned in either one of the two major German encyclopedias, Meyer's or Brockhaus. These two, put together, contain more words than the Britannica. But even when put together they had no word about either Mr. Liche or Dr. Fredlowski.

There was one more avenue to be explored. The date of publication of the letter in the elusive *Carlsruhe Scientific Journal* was given as 1878. The date of the publication of Mr. Osborn's book was 1924. After 1924 you could find references to the Liche-Fredlowski letter in many places. Logically, then, one could assume that books on Madagascar published between 1880 and 1924 should also make some reference to the letter, while books on Madagascar printed prior to 1880 would not, although they might make reference to the story itself, using a different source. This search also did not seem to lead anywhere for quite some time.

One of the classical works on Madagascar is a book known

under the name of *Robert Drury's Journal*. Robert Drury
was an Englishman, who, according to his own journal, was
born in London on July 24, 1687. When he grew up he became a sailor and in 1710 set out on the trip which was to
make him famous. He came to Madagascar, was taken captive, and remained on the island for fifteen years as a slave.
He saw native life before civilization had wrought any
changes; he saw much of the island. He also kept a journal
which is our only source for many things; though not a
learned man in any respect, he described animals and plants
so well that they could be identified later, and even native
words and names which he gave can be recognized, although
his rendering is anglicized, probably the way he pronounced
them himself. But in Drury's *Journal* there isn't a word
about such a plant, or any legend about such a plant, or even
any reference to a tribe called Mkodos.

Shifting from a classic to a work of painstaking description rendered by modern scientists I next went through
Madagascar au début du XX⁰ siècle, published in Paris in
1902 under the editorship of Professor of Medicine Raphaël
Blanchard. The botanical chapter in this symposium was
written by Emmanuel Drake del Castillo, the president of
the Société botanique de France; the zoological chapter by
Guillaume Grandidier, who was stationed on the island itself.
A very edifying book, a nicely printed book, and all that
—but no man-eating tree, no legend about man-eating trees,
no Mkodos. Instead, a large and beautiful map of the island
carefully keyed to show where Traveler's Trees abound and
where raphia palms grow.

Since Mr. Osborn had stressed in his book that the natives
talked about the man-eating tree and that every missionary
was aware of the story, I naturally looked for books by missionaries. There is one by Joseph Mullen, D.D., *Twelve
Months in Madagascar*, published in New York in 1875,
telling of the author's visit to missionaries in Madagascar.

But no tree, no legend, no Mkodos. There is another one by John Alden Houlder, entitled *Among the Malagasy; An unconventional record of missionary experience* (London, 1912). The author went to Madagascar in 1870 and stayed for several decades. Interesting report—but no tree, no legend, no Mkodos.

The next book I searched was a heavy tome by James Sibree with the title *A Naturalist in Madagascar,* published in Philadelphia in 1915, and based on *fifty* years of experience on the spot. Since Mr. Sibree was a missionary too, my hopes ran high. A missionary-naturalist with half a century of what appears to be almost uninterrupted residence should have something to tell. Sure, he had much to tell, but no tree, no legend, no Mkodos. Maybe a naturalist who was not a missionary might be a better source after all. So I picked up Walter D. Marcuse's *Through Western Madagascar in Quest of the Golden Bean.* Mr. Marcuse returned to England in 1912 and his book contains several chapters especially devoted to the fauna and flora of the island. But the final result was the same: no tree, no legend, no Mkodos.

It began to look as if no English-speaking missionary or naturalist had even ever heard of the story, and it seemed certain to me after reading all this that there was no native legend.

Having failed to obtain the *Carlsruhe Scientific Journal* which was supposed to have started it all, I decided that a survey of German books on Madagascar might be fruitful. The Germans at least ought to know their own periodical scientific literature. Well, in 1886 one Robert Hartmann published a book, *Madagaskar und die Inseln Seychellen,* devoted to the natural history of the island rather than its history. It turned out to be somewhat dull and "instructive" but competent and concise. Not a word about a man-eating tree, or about a story about a man-eating tree. Simply nothing. If there had been a publication of the Liche-

Fredlowski letter in a German scientific journal only half a dozen years earlier Hartmann would certainly have mentioned it.

Almost the last book on my pile was also in German. Its author was a Swiss naturalist, Dr. Conrad Keller; his book was *Reisebilder aus Ostafrika und Madagaskar* (*Travel Sketches from East Africa and Madagascar*), published in Leipzig in 1887. The author had been to the island twice, once in 1881-82, or very soon after the writing of the Liche-Fredlowski letter, and once again in 1886. Most of the book had been published in Swiss newspapers; the chapters had been actual letters which Dr. Keller wrote on his travels.

And one of Dr. Keller's reports contributed a great deal to the solution of the puzzle. He stated that something fantastic had been added to the actually marvelous flora of Madagascar in an alleged letter written "by a traveler Carl Liche whom I don't know" to "a certain Dr. Fredlowski" which was published "in a journal said to appear in Karlsruhe which I could not obtain." Because "the German original" could not be found Dr. Keller translated the letter from the *Antanarivo Annual and Madagascar Magazine for the Year 1881,* which he stated was a small local magazine published and printed by the missionaries. The condensed translation which he then gave shows very clearly that the letter published by Mr. Osborn was taken from that magazine and that the magazine's version is, in all probability, the original.

The facts are pretty clear by now. Of course the man-eating tree does not exist. There is no such tribe. The actual natives of Madagascar do not have such a legend. But at one time somebody made up the hoax, which was put into the only existing local magazine, possibly as a joke of some kind for the amusement of the readers who knew better. But it then got out of hand and the perpetrators thought it best to keep quiet. And if Mr. Chase Salmon Osborn, browsing around on the spot, had not resurrected it, the whole thing would have been forgotten a long time ago.

8: The Emperor's
Arcanum Magnum

RUDOLF II of Habsburg, emperor of the Holy Roman Empire, king of Hungary and of Bohemia, king of the Germans, duke of this and landgrave of that, was born in Vienna (in 1552) and educated by Jesuit scholars at the Court of Spain. Yet his later relations with Spain were not the best, and his favorite residence—especially later in life—was the old Hradčany castle in Prague. There the head of the Holy Roman Empire would often sit brooding in fits of depression which even his politest biographers had to label as "bordering on insanity." His courtiers, his generals, and his ambassadors might not be able to see the emperor for weeks at a time, but his astrologers and alchemists found access to the Imperial Chambers much more easily. True, other rulers of the time also supported an astrologer or two—one could never know when a horoscope might come in useful for a love affair, a siege, or a battle. They also took what later generations would dub a "calculated risk" on an occasional alchemist. If he did succeed in making gold, all the problems of the royal or ducal treasury would be solved; if not, the loss was small, consisting of a handful of gold and one fraudulent alchemist.

But Rudolf II did not support his astrologers and alchemists for material gain—or if material gain was mentioned it was for the purpose of placating the courtiers and generals. He was interested, intensely and fanatically interested, in their arts and knowledge. A horoscope was not a means of possibly outwitting a probable enemy who had failed to arm himself in like manner. It was a means of understanding the cosmos. Alchemy was not a means of possibly making gold, though the emperor would not have rejected such an achievement. It was the path to higher wisdom; it was to banish sickness and indecision, to prolong and aggrandize life and understanding. And repeatedly the emperor, who had been endowed with the proper upbringing of the Most Catholic Court of Spain, would confer with the High Rabbi Judah Loew of the Jewish congregation of Prague. Rabbi Loew was not only celebrated as a man of great scholarship and wisdom, he was also rumored to be a great magician and was credited with having made the *golem,* the living clay figure which was without speech but tireless and of unfailing strength and whose services must never be employed for secular purposes. The records, both the imperial and the rabbinical, state that the High Rabbi Loew was called to the palace to explain his religion to the churchmen or to defend his people against the accusation of ritual murder. But the records on both sides also candidly state that "after this they conferred on many things which were not spoken of afterwards." Rudolf, no doubt, inquired about magic and about the meanings of the Qabbala.

In less moody moments the emperor would support the fight against the Protestants, and simultaneously support Tycho Brahe and Johannes Kepler, two of the brightest stars on the firmament of the new astronomy which was to come— and both Protestants. And he would have the reports of countless men read to him, men who scoured all European cities, castles, and mansions for the emperor's collections, for Rudolf was an indefatigable collector. His family finally decided, in 1606, that he was unfit to rule and declared one of his younger brothers, Archduke Matthias, head of the family. The decision was indubitably correct and justified, but the collections Rudolf had brought together, especially the art collections, could have been the envy of anybody at any time.

There was just one item which Rudolf failed to obtain, even though his representative was authorized to pay the fantastic sum of 4000 florins for it—a thousand florins more than Tycho Brahe received per year. The unobtainable item was not a work of art; in fact it was not man-made at all. It was what was then called a *curiosum naturae,* a gigantic nut.

Every once in a while the currents of the sea would wash one of these gigantic nuts ashore, in India or on the coast of Ceylon, or on the beaches of the Maldive Islands which lie to the southwest of the Indian triangle. They also occurred— oh, so infrequently—farther to the east; for example, on the coast of Java. All the princes of the Far East considered them the most valuable possession a prince could have, and a ship-load of merchandise was considered proper pay for one. A Dutch admiral who had been victorious in a battle against the Portuguese was presented with one of these nuts by a native ruler—nothing else would serve to express the grati-tude felt for this victory. The Dutch admiral, Wolfert Hermanszen, who beat the Portuguese admiral Andrea For-tado de Mendoza in 1602 and received a specimen of the fabulous nut for his victory, finally returned to Holland, taking his prize along. It was this nut, the only one in Europe, which Rudolf II coveted, but the family would not sell; it was too valuable a possession. The Dutch and the Portuguese and the various natives might have many differ-ences, but they were all agreed that the man who was lucky enough to get hold of a *Coco do Mar,* as the Portuguese called it, or *Maldivische Cocus-noot,* as it was known by the Dutch, would not part with it again.

It must be admitted that even nowadays such a nut is a most impressive specimen. With a circumference of over a yard and a weight approaching fifty pounds, it is now estab-

lished as the largest seed of any plant. When the outer
leathery covering is still in place, the coco-de-mer—the
French term is the one which is now most generally used—
resembles the much smaller coconut in shape. But when the
outer skin has been removed it displays a strange shape,
reminiscent of the shape of the "meat" of a walnut. It
almost looks as if two nuts had coalesced. Inside this apparent
double hull you then find nut meat of similar shape, resembling that of the coconut but much softer in texture. Taste is
said to be singularly absent—"a whitish uninviting watery
pulp for which I would not trade a single good hazelnut" is
the opinion of a recent naturalist who actually tasted one.

But the Malays, the Burmese, and the Chinese, and whoever else offered pearls by the bagful and silks by the boat-
load for these nuts, did not trade for delicacies. They were
after the supreme remedy of the ages. The nut meat was first
dried and then ground up with ivory, or with deer antlers,
or with red coral, in various and strange proportions.
Depending on the admixtures this was an effective, nay,
infallible, remedy for paralysis or stroke; it cured gall-
bladder troubles and hemorrhoids. In addition to that, and
most important for many of the princes who sought and
bought it, the coco-de-mer destroyed any poison which might
be mixed into food or drink, just as the horn of the unicorn
was supposed to do.

Naturally it has no true medicinal value; its reputation
was based solely on the factors of extreme rarity, sheer and
impressive size, strange shape, and complete ignorance as to
origin. It was not even known then whether this was actually
a nut, a seed of a tree; there were some who held that it
might be mineral. Presumably this idea originated with an
experimenter who had decided that, if it were a nut, it could
be planted and would produce a strange tree of some kind
which would bear additional nuts, thereby providing a lifetime of luxury for its owner. Whoever tried that must have
been disappointed, for the nut probably failed to sprout;

we now know that even under the most favorable conditions it takes over a year for the seedling to show signs of life.

Rudolf II probably did not offer 4000 florins to protect his

Coco-de-mer, or "Solomon's sea nut," with its outer skin removed to
show the deep indentation

life against disease or to ward off poisoners; unlike most
other princes of his time he does not seem to have been
unduly afraid of poisoning. Either poisoning was not much
practiced in Vienna and in the Hradčany castle, or else he

relied on the alicorns, the horns of unicorns, which he did possess. But the nut certainly possessed magic properties too. Nobody could say with any certainty just what they were, but to a mystic of that time the shape may have suggested a unification of the male and female principles, which was unique and therefore significant, no matter whether it was vegetable or mineral. And wasn't this very uncertainty another parallel to the alicorn? The alicorn, like that strange fruit of the seas, was valuable medicine against many diseases and an unfailing protector against poison. Though it was known to come from a very rare and very strange beast, the alicorn was somehow both animal (in origin) and mineral (in hardness and appearance). And the very best alicorn was dug from the ground, which enhanced its mineral qualities.

The reasoning about King Solomon's Nut—to give it another name then in use—must have been along these lines, and nobody could successfully contradict any of it, unless he could have stated from personal experience and observation that this was an ordinary, though gigantic, tree nut, which had grown on an ordinary, though probably large, tree that could be found in this or that location. But from the day the first coco-de-mer which had drifted ashore somewhere was picked up as a curiosity by somebody, until the middle of the eighteenth century, literally nobody knew where it grew.

One area of the globe was under evident suspicion. The nut had to grow somewhere in the Far East, where expensive spices could be plucked off bushes and trees all year round, where, as some averred in hushed tones, gems were lying around as pebbles on the beaches. There, in the utmost distance of blue seas and steady winds, where the colors of the sunset faded fast to give way to low-hanging stars in the flower-scented night, somewhere in this vast and scarcely known realm the tree with the wonder nuts had to grow. There also grew, as some told, strange bushes with leaves which did not fall off but flew away as butterflies when their time came. This was also the area where, as one had heard, the terrible poison tree, the *oepas* of the Dutch, existed, itself alive but inimical to all other life.

In short, it had to be on or near Java. And the priests of the Javanese claimed that they knew where it grew, not on their own island, but some distance to the south of it.

But I am already cribbing from the book which for more than a hundred years from the time of its publication was virtually the only, and in any event the most reliable source about the natural history of that area, the *Herbarium amboinense*. Admiring savants in Europe who read and reread it avidly did not even refer to its author by his name; they called him the *Plinius indicus*, the Pliny of the Indies. The author of the *Herbarium* did not know about this appellation, of course, since the work which caused all this admiration had been printed after his death. He had simply stated his name on the title page in its Latinized version of Georgius Everhardus Rumphius, and somebody had added his title, *Oud Koopman en Raadspersoon*—Senior Merchant and Council Member.

Only Dutch readers who read the right-hand columns of the work were even faintly interested in the fact that the author had been an *Oud Koopman* in their East India Company. The others, who read the Latin left-hand columns of the book, paid no attention to the Latin designation of *Mercator Senior*. It was neither title nor affiliation which counted, but the book itself. If anybody wanted to know something about a plant growing in this distant wonderland, whether for sound commercial reasons connected with the spice trade, or because of the dictates of intellectual curiosity, he had to reach for the *Herbarium amboinense*. There he could find information about the strange *Myrmecodia* (discovered by Rumphius). This plant is now called an epiphyte, which means that it grows on the branches of trees but not as a parasite—it does not take anything from the tree except a little space on a branch. The *Myrmecodia* might be described as looking somewhat like a small pineapple. The

bulbous growth, however, is anything but edible; it consists
of tough woody fibers, with innumerable tunnels and holes.
And the tunnels are inhabited by ants which defend their
plant fiercely against any intruder. We now know that each
species of "ant-plant"—there are quite a number—is inhabited
by "its" species of ants which will make their home in only
the proper plant and no other. Or the reader of the
Herbarium would come across such an astonishingly accurate statement as the one that the cycad trees, though they
look like palms, are closer in organization to the tree ferns.

If the problem was not strictly botanical the researcher
would reach for the only other printed book of the *Plinius
indicus,* entitled *D'Amboinsche Rariteitkamer (The Amboina Cabinet of Rarities)* which existed both in Dutch and
in German. There the reader could find the first picture of
a horseshoe crab (eastern version, *Limulus moluccanus*), the
first description of the pearly nautilus, the first mention of
coconut "pearls" (small stones which occasionally form inside
coconuts), and the statement that the butterfly bushes do not
actually bear leaves which change into butterflies but that
there are butterflies which look like leaves when they fold
their wings. The *Rariteitkamer* also contains what is probably the earliest mention of the crab now called *Birgus latro,*
or else "robber crab," a big fat crab of the general shape and
size of a lobster, but heavier, which eats coconuts only. It
comes out of the sea for the coconuts, carefully and slowly
tears off the thick cover of fibers, hammers its way with the
aid of the large claws through one of the weak spots on top
of the nut, and then reaches inside for the meat with the
small claws of the legs. It is now accepted as a fact that *Birgus
latro* even climbs trees and patiently saws through the stem
of a nut if no ripe nuts are lying around on the ground.

I know that "interrupting the narrative" is something
which magazine editors and literary critics, even in their
most lenient moods, consider old-fashioned if nothing worse.

But, having already strayed to some extent, I feel that it would border on injustice if I did not say something about the man who wrote these books. I consider this all the more necessary since standard reference works, like the Encyclopaedia Britannica, do not even mention him.

Georg Eberhard Rumpf, then, was born in 1627, day unknown. We know the year of his birth only because he himself mentioned it in a letter to his superiors in the Dutch East India Company, and we can infer from the words *van Hanau* which follow the signature of this letter that Hanau in Germany was his birthplace. Actually linguistic usage was not so clear-cut as to permit this deduction; the *van Hanau* in the letter, as well as the words *mijn vaderlijke stad Hanau* ("my fathertown Hanau") in the *Herbarium,* only mean that Rumpf came from that city. He may well have been born elsewhere. His father, Augustus Rumpf, had his son baptized as a Protestant and enrolled him at the Gymnasium (High School) of Hanau, where the emphasis was on classical literature and ancient languages. At the age of nineteen, one year after graduating, young Rumpf went to Holland. Apparently he spoke Dutch, and this, coupled with the fact that Hanau and vicinity were a place of refuge for Dutch Protestants, makes it probable that the family was Dutch.

A number of inadvertent adventures followed. Young Rumpf enlisted as a soldier with troops which were supposed to defend the Republic of Venice. The men were embarked at a Dutch port after having been told that the best and easiest way to reach Venice was by sea, even though it meant a longer trip than the overland route. What the men were not told was that they were to be sent to Brazil to defend Dutch claims against Portuguese encroachment. It did not matter much, for they never got there; their ship was captured by a Portuguese warship and the men were brought to Lisbon as prisoners of war. Released after two years, Rumpf returned to Holland and enlisted again, this time with the armed forces of the Dutch East India Company. After several delays and a long slow trip the future *Plinius indicus* set foot on the beach of the island of Amboina, then the center of Dutch activities in the East. The year was 1653, his age was twenty-six. After three years of service he received his first promotion; he was made *vaandrig*, or cornet. One year later he requested transfer to the civilian branch of the company; the request was granted and Rumpf was made *Onderkoopman*, Junior Merchant.

At that time he started his first literary project, a Malay-Dutch dictionary. By then he spoke Malay fluently. Strangely enough he did not write it with Latin letters but with Arabic script, which he must have thought better adapted to Malay sounds. Promotion followed in 1662, when Rumpf became a full-fledged *Koopman*, or Merchant. By then he had seen so many new and interesting things that he decided to write about them. He wrote to the regional directors, telling them about his plan and requesting permission to buy some books and instruments in Amsterdam. The letter was approved and forwarded to Amsterdam. But there was red tape even then. The regional director ordered that any parcels for Koopman Rumphius *op het packhuys sullen worden gevisiteerd* (shall be inspected at the warehouse). The company had a monopoly and took it seriously. Koopman Rumphius did not mind having his parcels inspected and happily went to work. His only worry was that his eyesight seemed to be failing. In 1670 it turned out that his worry was justified; cataracts developed in both eyes. One was completely blinded and the other one very nearly so. And in those days nothing could be done about cataracts.

The company did what it could to improve matters. Rumpf was called to the main settlement, Amboina Kasteel, to live. He was promoted to Senior Merchant and simultaneously relieved of all duties. He was appointed to the court of justice so that his salary could be continued. His son, Koopman Paulus Augustus Rumphius, received a new assignment, that of seeing that his father completed his books. A secretary for Oud Koopman Rumphius was selected from among the clerks, and the artist Philips van Eijck was called from Amsterdam to assist with the illustrations.

But all the help that money could furnish could not avert several disasters. On Chinese New Year in 1674 the older Rumpf, his wife, and his youngest daughter attended the Chinese celebration. A fireworks display was scheduled to be put on after dark. Rumpf, unable to see the spectacle, decided that he would rather go for his customary evening walk. While he was away an earthquake struck the area; Rumpf, being in the open, was not even injured, but his wife and daughter both died. More than a decade later, in 1687, a fire broke out at Amboina Kasteel, consuming the greater part of the nearly finished manuscript. A few portions were saved, of a few other portions copies had been made which were elsewhere on the island, and after a few weeks of dejection Rumpf decided to write over again what had been destroyed.

In 1692 the manuscript for the first six books of the *Herbarium amboinense* was put aboard a ship which set sail for Batavia. From there the manuscript was to be shipped to Amsterdam to be printed. In 1701 the rest of the manuscript left for Amsterdam. And one year later, on June 15, 1702, Senior Merchant Rumpf died on Amboina, completely blind, very lonely, and convinced that he had failed in life.

It sounds like a chapter from an overplotted bad novel, but the first shipment of the manuscript was almost lost once more. The ship which sailed from Batavia for Holland with the manuscript aboard was the *Waterland*. The *Waterland* never reached Europe; she was sighted, engaged, and sunk by a French vessel. It was fortunate that the manuscript had not been shipped to Holland directly from Amboina, since it was preserved only because of the stopover in Batavia. The Governor-General, Joannes Camphuys, had been hearing about Rumpf and his work for years. When the ship from

Amboina arrived he read the manuscript, or at least portions
of it. And being an experienced man who knew all the
hazards of long voyages in wooden ships, with enemies and
pirates on the high seas, he ordered the whole manuscript
copied before he parted with it. The manuscript which had
been written on Amboina sank with the *Waterland*; the copy
made in Batavia reached Amsterdam a year later.

In volume VI of the work which was almost destroyed twice
you can find Rumpf's report on the coco-de-mer. It is chapter
VIII of the twelfth book, consisting of eight folio pages of
text and one more folio page with a picture of the nut. The
picture is inferior to the other illustrations in the *Herbarium*
and actually contains a mistake: the two halves of the nut
are shown as completely separated. Obviously the artist did
not have a specimen to draw but had to go by descriptions.
And nobody who saw the picture before it went to the
engraver's shop had ever seen a specimen either.

Whatever criticism one may make of the picture, there
can be none of the text; it is what Carolus Linnaeus said
about the whole book: *solidissimus*. As has been mentioned,
the Javanese claimed to know where the nut grew. One version of the story which Rumpf heard is reasonably simple:
the tree grows deep under water all around the island of
Sumatra and especially in a certain bay on the southern
shore. Occasionally it can be seen in quiet, clear water from
a boat. But if you look for the tree under water or try to get
closer to it by diving you'll surely drown.

There was, however, a more elaborate story which Rumpf
repeated with the introductory remark that this was "the
worse fable." The natives told that the tree which bore the
sea nut was unique; there was only one like it in the world.
It grew in the open sea beyond Java. The bough of the
Pausengi Tree, as they called it, rises above the waves and
in it a bird called the Geruda has built its nest. This Geruda
is the same as the Griffin and it flies about over the islands,
taking elephants, tigers, rhinoceri, "or other large animals"

with its claws and bringing them to its nest in the sea for its young to eat. One cannot approach the place where the Pausengi Tree grows—or rather one can approach it only too easily, for all the currents in the ocean converge there. A ship that comes near will drift helplessly to the tree and be unable to return. The sailors who thus have an opportunity of seeing the tree can never tell their tale, for they will die of hunger and thirst, unless they fall victim to the Geruda bird first.

For fear of being pulled to the Pausengi Tree none of the Javanese dared to sail farther than a few miles out to sea; as long as they could see their own island they were able to return to it. But in spite of every precaution, some fishermen had been caught in one of the currents and had drifted out to the tree. They succeeded in approaching the Geruda bird unseen and clung to its feathers when it took to the air. As the bird swooped down on some prey on Java they released their hold and, after making their way back to their villages, told what had happened to them. And that was how the location of the Pausengi Tree and the nest of the Geruda became known.[1]

Now the sea nut from the Pausengi Tree had the strange characteristic of moving against currents, which is how it could reach the shore of Java. But even then it still had some power of locomotion left; if the slope of the beach was gentle the nut would cross it and hide itself in the underbrush, well away from the water. Because of this behavior the nuts were even more rare; they were usually spied by men only because the dogs barked and yelped at the moving nut. At that point

---

[1] Here is precisely the same story that you probably know from the *Arabian Nights*, and which was also told independently in the medieval German romance *Herzog Ernst von Schwaben*. All the story elements are there: the giant bird which carries elephants and rhinoceri to its young, the escape from danger by riding the bird, the place to which all ships are irresistibly drawn. The only difference is that the Javanese version contains converging currents, while the Western versions utilize the Mountain of Lodestone. It may be added that the location of the Mountain of Lodestone was thought to be the Sunda Sea.

Rumpf departed from straight reporting and remarked dryly: *"Uit welke Fabel de Lezer afnemen kan, waarom deze vrugt zoo hoog geëstimeert, en zoo duur gebouden werden";* which may be rendered in English as: "From this fable the reader may conclude why this fruit is so highly esteemed and is so dearly sought."

But this last item of the story, which made Rumpf add what was for him an especially caustic remark, is probably not entirely a fable. It may not have applied to the coco-de-mer, if only because the giant nut is too rare, but it does apply to the ordinary coconut. A watcher endowed with enough patience to sit quietly in the moonlight on a beach in those islands may actually witness the incredible spectacle of a coconut drifting ashore and, after some time, suddenly ascending the beach and beginning to crawl across the sand, shambling and hesitantly, until it has disappeared in the underbrush. Of course the nut did not suddenly acquire the power of locomotion, however feebly; for the "motive force" is something else. Ironically it is provided by something that Rumpf himself knew, the crab he called *Cancer crumenatus,* the *Birgus latro* of our books. The crab does drag coconuts across the beach to a place where the waves cannot interfere with its tedious job of opening and eating them.

Having related all the various stories and items he had heard about the rare sea nut, Rumpf was faced by the necessity of forming an opinion of his own. If you trimmed every story and report down to its bare essentials you had two facts, one negative and one positive. The negative fact was that nobody had ever seen the tree which produced the nut. The positive fact was that every nut ever found was found at the seashore. Combining these two Rumpf concluded that it had to be a product of the sea and he imagined a plant, growing on the sea bottom not too far from the shore where the nuts appeared. Obviously he could not tell how the plant looked, but he tended to think of it as quite simple in shape. As for the location, he believed that the plant grew especially

frequently in the area of the Maldive islands, which would
account for the Dutch name *Maldivische Cocus-noot.*

At the time Rumpf was writing his *Herbarium,* and in fact
even before he was born, the place where the coco-de-mer
actually grew was more or less clearly marked on nautical
charts. It was the group of islands which is now known as
the Seychelles. The Dutch name of the nut had been wrong,
one is tempted to say, by just one archipelago. The Seychelles
are the first group of islands which a traveler sailing on a
southwesterly course from the Maldives would reach. The
trip would be fairly long, around 1300 miles as the sea gull
flies, but there is only water between the two island groups.
To go due west from the Seychelles to the African coast is a
trip of almost equal length, and the isolation of this group of
islands must have been partly responsible for their late
discovery.

The earliest charts showing an entry of islands that fits the
Seychelles are of Portuguese origin; they are the charts of
Alberto Cantino and Nicolas Caneirio, dated 1502. During
the course of the sixteenth century islands occupying the
approximate position of the actual Seychelles—it was so hard
to measure longitude that an error of 5 to 10 degrees was
rather customary—were entered on a total of eighteen charts.
But the first recorded visit took place in 1609. None of the
earlier sea captains seems to have made an attempt to land,
not necessarily because there was other and more pressing
business on hand. Sea captains did not always write down
everything they knew and it may have been routine knowledge among them that the island or islands one might
encounter some 600 miles to the north of Madagascar had
no inhabitants. On uninhabited islands there was no possibility of trade of any kind, and one could not even take
slaves. Hence there was no reason to land.

It was in January 1609 that an English ship commanded
by Captain John Jourdain arrived in the archipelago. A boat

was sent ashore for fresh water and the beaching of that boat by the water search party constitutes the first known landing of any vessel on any of the Seychelles Islands. Both Captain Jourdain and his shipmate Revett told interesting things about the big land tortoises their men found,[2] but they did not quite know what to do with an uninhabited island either. And they missed the one on which grew the trees bearing the coco-de-mer.

That nobody was much interested is probably best shown by the time interval that elapsed between the first and the second recorded visits: it was a hundred and thirty-three years!

The second visitor, in 1742, was the French captain Lazare Picault, who returned to the islands in 1744 for the purpose of annexing them formally to France. He acted as an agent for the governor of Mauritius, Mahé de la Bourdonnais, and being a perceptive scoundrel or else well versed in politics (though he couldn't spell), he named the whole group of islands Les Îles de la Bourdonnais. More than that, he called the largest island Mahé. But he explored only a part of the group and also succeeded in missing the one with the coco-de-mer trees.

It took a little while for the French to begin to think about the new group of islands which they had acquired. When they did so, they first changed the name—it was thought in Paris or in Versailles that having the largest island named Mahé was enough honor for the governor of Mauritius, and in 1756 the group as a whole was named for Moreau de Séchelles, then *contrôleur des finances* under King Louis XV. Simultaneously the Duc de Praslin ordered a more thorough investigation of the islands with emphasis on the question of what use they might be. The first result was that the second largest island received the name of Praslin. The man who explored Praslin Island was an engineer named Barré. Hacking his way through the jungle, he

[2] See Chapter 12.

came across enormous palm trees, almost 100 feet tall, with
fronds measuring close to 30 feet from their tips to the base
of the leaf stalk. And among these enormous, rigid, and fan-
shaped fronds there hung clusters of enormous palm nuts.
The source of the coco-de-mer had been discovered at last.

Monsieur Barré was a perceptive man too, but not quite

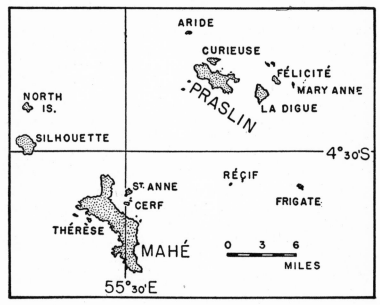

The Seychelles Islands

The island of Praslin is the only remaining natural habitat of the palm
Lodoicea seychellarum

perceptive enough. He took a shipload of coco-de-mer to
India, no doubt with visions of a life of luxury for himself,
his potential mistresses, his children and children's children.
But a whole shipload of coco-de-mer was too much; when the
prospective customers saw the abundance of treasure the
price of the coco-de-mer declined rapidly and permanently.
If the French had known what could be found on Praslin
Island they might, with rigid export control and careful one-

at-a-time trading, have brought prosperity to their national treasury on coco-de-mer alone. Having missed that chance because of Barré's careless action, they began to wonder what else might grow on the islands. The intendant of Île de France (Mauritius), Monsieur Pierre Poivre, was shrewder and obviously far more experienced than Barré. He realized that the Seychelles were outside the hurricane paths, hence a safe place for plantations. The climate being what it is, spices should grow there; one could compete with the Dutch monopoly on those. Spice plantations—especially for vanilla— were started on various islands and kept strictly secret. The Dutch would not be able to help noticing after a while that spices from other sources were appearing on the market, but nobody was to know where these sources were located. When, in 1778, a ship flying the Union Jack approached, the French felt that their secret might become known and they hurriedly set fire to their spice plantations. After the ship had landed it turned out to be a French slaver who had run up the British flag because he thought the British might have taken possession of the islands while he was at sea.

His suspicions were not really wrong, merely too early by a few decades. The British did take possession of the islands in 1810 and became the formal owners four years later by the Treaty of Paris of 1814.

As for the islands themselves, Mahé is not only the largest, with an area of 53 square miles, it is also the most centrally located and crowned by the highest and third highest mountains in the archipelago, measuring 2993 and 2390 feet, respectively. Praslin, with an area of 27 square miles, is second in size and the center of a well-defined subgroup of islands. Next in size in this subgroup is La Digue (named after one of the ships which went there in 1744), with 4 square miles; the others in this subgroup are named East and West Silver, Aride, Félicité, Mary Anne, and Curieuse, the last of these names also being taken from one of the ships. A second subgroup consists of only two islands, of which Silhou-

ette is the larger. With an area of 8 square miles, it ranks
third among the Seychelles and has the second highest mountain, 2473 feet high, and called Mon Plaisir, although I don't
know whose pleasure it happened to be. It was first seen by
Captain John Jourdain on January 10, 1609. The other
island of that subgroup is North Island.

Naturally, since the Seychelles changed hands, many of the
smaller islands no longer bear their original names. The
island originally named Île des Oiseaux is now called Bird
Island, which is at least a straight translation. But the Île des
Vaches Marines ("sea-cow island," so named from the dugongs
which were found there) became plain Denis Island, which
sounds like something in some river back of town.

All the islands are of granite, largely hornblende, indicating great age. In fact, the Seychelles look like left-overs
of a large continent of the past. A hundred years ago geologists were convinced that there had once been a continent
stretching from Madagascar to the Indian mainland, and
that Madagascar itself, Mauritius, Réunion, the Comores,
Aldabra, the Seychelles, and the Maldives are all just remains
of this "Lemuria." But in spite of appearances more modern
geological ideas tend to deny that a whole continent can
simply disappear under the sea. However, these same more
recent ideas encourage the concept that the continents are
not solidly anchored to the earth but may move. When such
movements take place, the reasoning runs, portions of the
continent may become detached and be left behind, as
Madagascar looks like a piece of Africa that was left behind
when the continent as a whole shifted toward the west. The
Seychelles might well be another such split-off portion which
lasted for a while as a large island a few thousand square
miles in extent and then was partly flooded.

The palm bearing the coco-de-mer would then be a typical
"living fossil" which happened to survive on this split-off
area while it became extinct elsewhere. It is true that this
palm, though individually large and powerful and almost

indestructible, does not seem to be able to compete with other tropical plants. After all, it did not even survive all over the Seychelles islands but only on Praslin. Even the trees on the neighboring island of Curieuse are said to have been introduced artificially.

Lodoicea seychellarum, to use its scientific name,[3] is remarkable for many reasons, most of them somehow connected with size. The tall trunk of the adult tree has been called "as hard as iron and equally resistant to all outside influences." But it takes a long time for a Lodoicea to become an adult tree.

To begin at the beginning: the nuts need seven to eight years to ripen. When they are planted at the end of this period it is at least a year before the seedling appears. The seedling does not necessarily come up in the spot where the nut was planted; it is almost the rule that it grows horizontally underground for several yards before it breaks through the surface. Then it takes thirty-five to forty years before the plant flowers for the first time. Even then it is by no means adult; in fact it isn't old enough to have developed a trunk. Every adult Lodoicea, therefore, must be considerably more than a century old. Some of the larger specimens which are now growing on Praslin may have sprouted at the time Captain Jourdain's men were looking for fresh water on another island. As in the ginkgo, another living fossil, the two sexes are strictly separated; a Lodoicea is either male or female. Since this means that only about half of the adult plants can bear fruit the possible rate of reproduction is slowed down some more.

Professor Carl Chun, the leader of the German oceanographic expedition on *S.S. Valdivia* in 1898-99, who went to Praslin specifically for Lodoicea, did not hesitate to write in his account of the expedition that Lodoicea might well be

[3] The name was given by Jacques Julien Houtou de Labillardière, who was the naturalist of the expedition sent out to locate the lost expedition of La Pérouse. The name Lodoicea is a modification of Laodikē, the daughter of Priam; I can't tell just what Labillardière had in mind when he picked it.

extinct by now if it had not been for John Horne, the
director of the Botanical Garden on Mauritius. In 1875 John
Horne convinced the government of Queen Victoria that
something irreplaceable would be gone if Lodoicea were
permitted to disappear from the islands. In response to his

The palm *Lodoicea seychellarum.* At right, a "young" specimen about
40 years old

strongly worded request a large valley on Praslin where most
of the biggest specimens grew, and all of the island of
Curieuse, were declared crown property, and the necessary
laws for protecting the plants growing elsewhere on Praslin
were made.

John Horne, as well as other British botanists, realized
perfectly well that a threatened species can be saved in two

ways. One is to protect it where it happens to occur; the other is to extend its range so that a local accident like a forest fire can have only local effects. Lodoicea nuts were planted in various localities that looked suitable, like Mauritius, and in a botanical garden in Ceylon. They did sprout and take root, but the plant grows so slowly that most visitors were disappointed when they saw them. And although the giant nuts have drifted ashore in Borneo, Java, and Sumatra for many centuries, and not all of them could have been found, there is no known case of a Lodoicea growing on any of these islands.

King Solomon's nut still retains at least one secret—why it failed to spread from its last retreat. And the existence of Lodoicea still hinges on its continued survival on two tiny islands.

Part Three

SURVIVORS

Every creature is better alive than dead, men
and moose and pine-trees, and he who under-
stands it aright will rather preserve its life
than destroy it.

—Henry David Thoreau

9: The Case of the Cahow

THE Bermudas, no longer "vex'd" in the age of airplanes and radar and other navigational devices, began their career in human affairs in a manner which did not help to ingratiate them with sailors. They were discovered because Señor Juan Bermudez, en route from España to Cuba with a shipload of hogs, was shipwrecked there, early in the sixteenth century.

The next shipwreck was that of Mr. Henry May of England in 1593. In 1609 Sir George Somers, one of the founders of the South Virginia Company, was also shipwrecked—and took possession of the islands for the king of England. For a number of years the islands bore the name of Somers Islands (often spelled "Summer Islands," possibly as a well-intentioned pun), but the name of the original, though involuntary, discoverer finally won out.

The Bermudas have several claims to fame, in addition to their near-ideal climate and the long list of ships wrecked there in the past. One is that the first coins in the Western Hemisphere were struck there. The values impressed on them followed British usage, but the pictures on the coins were ships (unwrecked) and hogs.

Lying at the edge of the Sargasso Sea, the islands mark the northernmost point where corals are actively building. Unlike other lonely islands with a mild clime and potentially luxuriant vegetation the Bermudas did not have an interesting or even an abundant animal life. But sea birds nested there in enormous numbers and one variety very nearly caused sailors to believe that the islands were not only dangerous but haunted to boot. In 1603, before Sir George Somers established his settlement, the galleon of Captain Diego Ramirez was caught in a storm and driven in the direction of the islands. By luck or by skill Señor Ramirez brought his ship into a natural harbor:

The first night that I anchored in the bay, I sent a small boat to an inlet to look for water, but none was found. At dusk, such a shrieking and din filled the air that fear seized us. Only one variety of bird makes this noise, but the concerted yell is terrible and standing out from it were individual voices shouting *diselo! diselo!* ["tell 'em, tell 'em"] One seaman said to me: "What is this devil trying to tell me? Out with it! Let's hear what it is!" I replied: *"A la!* These are the devils reported to be about Bermuda. The sign of the cross at them! We are Christians!" While we were in this confusion, the men of the small boat rushed up, exclaiming in their alarm, "What devils are these? The boat's rudder is broken." I ordered another one to be made immediately, because in the morning the coast had to be searched for water. One Venturilla, a negro, was sent on shore with lantern and axe to cut a piece of cedar. The moment he landed and entered the bush, he set up such a yell, that I shouted: "The devil is carrying off the negro! Everybody ashore!" The men jumped into a boat and rushed to the spot where the negro was brandishing his lantern and his fists against the birds, and mingling his yells with theirs. The birds, meanwhile, attracted by the light, dashed against him, so that he could not keep clear of them even with a club. Neither could the men of the relief party. More than 500 birds were brought off to the ship that night, and, having gone through hot water and been plucked, proved to be very fat and fine. Thereafter a capture was made every evening. The birds were so plentiful that 4000 could be taken in a single bag. The men relished them enough to eat them all the time, and when we left we brought away more than 1000 well dried and salted for the voyage.

William Beebe, who published this excerpt from Captain Ramirez's account (in the *Bulletin* of the New York Zoological Society, November-December 1935), did not say where the account could be found in print, so I don't know what finally happened either to Captain Ramirez or to Venturilla, who had to stand on a dark and stormy beach with a lantern, fighting off multitudes of sea birds that were probably as frightened as he was.

In any event this was mankind's first encounter with a bird that came to be called cahow from its call. Unfortunately for the bird the encounter was typical. The sailors' food in those days was monotonous, often poor in quality, and insufficient in quantity. An island full of tasty sea birds was a sailor's dream, well worth the risk of a few cliffs and reefs. Elsewhere ships' captains went out of their way for such bird islands, "to victuall themselves," as they called it. The great auk was brought close to extinction by this need for provisions for long and tedious voyages, though its final extermination was caused by a natural catastrophe.

The cahow never caused such "victualling stops," because it did not last long enough. Unlike the other bird islands, the Bermudas were settled, and the settlers ate cahow themselves. Even worse, the settlers had been preceded by two of the most destructive animals in existence. The very first ship to reach the islands had carried a cargo of live pigs. And if this ship was miraculously free of rats, other ships were not. Either pigs or rats spell the end of a ground-nesting bird colony. But the existence of the cahow was not yet endangered, in spite of the strange fact that this far-flying bird was restricted to the Bermuda islands as a breeding place. What saved it then is that its breeding place is not a single large island, as, for example, Ceylon, but a cluster of islands, large, medium-sized, and small, plus islets, tiny islets, cliffs and rocks.

That the activities of the egg-devouring hogs were realized

early can be seen from the report written on July 15, 1610, by the Secretary-Elect for Virginia, William Strachey, who had been one of Sir George Somers' party.

A kind of webbe-footed Fowle there is, of the bigness of an *English* green Plouer, or Sea-Meawe, which all the Summer wee saw not, and in the darkest nights of Nouember and December (for in the night they only feed) they would come forth, but not flye farre from home, and houering in the ayre, and oure the Sea, made a strange hollow and harsh howling. . . . These gather themselues together and breed in those Ilands which are high, and so farre alone into the Sea, that the Wilde Hogges cannot swimme ouer them, and there in the ground they haue their Burrowes. . . .

If the distance had only prevented the settlers too from following the birds! But the people had boats and ingenuity, as Mr. Strachey reported:

Our men found a prettie way to take them, which was by stand-ing on the Rockes or Sands by the Sea side, and hollowing, laugh-ing, and making the strangest out-cry that possibly they could; with the noyse whereof the Birds would come flocking to that place, and settle vpon the very armes and head of him that so cryed, and still creepe neerer and neerer, answering the noyse themselues: by which our men would weigh them with their hand, and which weighed heauiest they took for the Best, and let the others alone, and so our men would take twentie dozen in two houres of the chiefest of them: and they were a good and well relished Fowle, fat and full as a partridge. In January wee had great store of their Egges, which are as great as an Hennes Egge, and so fashioned and white shelled, and haue no difference in yolke nor white from an Hennes Egge. There are thousands of these birds, and two or three Ilands full of their Burrowes, whether at any time (in two hours warning) wee could send our Cockboat, and bringe home as many as would serue the whole Company . . .

The preacher Lewis Hughes again stressed the "great abundance of the Cahouye" in 1614. There must still have

been large numbers in 1619 when Nathaniel Butler, then
governor of the islands, remarked, "For the cahowe (for so
soundes his voice), it is a night bird, and all the daye long
lies hidd in holes of the rocks, whence both themselves and
their young are in great numbers extracted with ease, and
prove (especially the young) so pleaseinge in a dish, as
ashamed I am to tell how many dozen of them haue been
devoured by some of our northern stomacks, even at one
only meale." He added, about another bird which is unhelp-
fully labeled "the egge-bird," that "many thousands of [its]
egges are yearely eaten, and many more would be, but that
by strict inhibition, they are preserved."

   The remark about the inhibition can only refer to Butler's
predecessor's gubernatorial "Proclamation against the spoile
of Cahowes," which was the direct result of a famine caused
by the rats. In his *Historye of the Bermudaes,* Butler gave
a specific incident of famine measures.

Whilst this Pinnace was on her way for England, scarcetie and
famine every day more and more prevayleinge upon the sickly
colony, caused the governour to look well about him; in the beginning of the newe yeare [1615], therefore 150 persons of the
most ancient, sick and weake, wer sent into Coopers Iland, ther
to be relieved by the comeinge in of the sea-birds, especially the
Cahowes, wher, by this half hunger-starved company, they wer
found in infinite numbers, and so tame and amazed they are,
that upon the least howeteinge or noyce, they would fall downe,
and light upon their shoulders as they went, and leggs as they
satt, suffering themselves to be caught. . . .

   By 1621, the famine over, the Bermuda Company enacted
a law which obligated the governor and the officers of the
company to preserve the birds "by reserving to them those
Ilands whereunto they resort." Good will did exist, but the
combination of pigs and rats, unrestrained early hunting and
emergency measures during a famine, had done its work.
The much-discussed Captain John Smith mentioned both
the cahow and the "egge-bird" in his *Generall Historie of*

Virginia, New-England, and the Summer Isles (1624), but he was just repeating established information. The second edition, in 1629 (which I have not seen myself), is said to state that cahows and egg birds are "all gone."

The cahow, then, disappeared sometime between 1620 and 1625.

The next chapter in the history of this bird might well be entitled "Confusion" but though it lasted a long time in years—almost three centuries—the story can be told fairly quickly. Scientists reading Mr. William Strachey's account and Governor Butler's *Historye* had to conclude that there had been an abundant sea bird of distinct habits and characteristics, breeding on these islands only. Since the descriptions were not detailed enough for proper classification, no scientific name could be assigned to it; it was just the "extinct Bermuda cahow." Nor could one say with any certainty what kind of bird it had been, though it seemed likely that it was a petrel.

The period of confusion began a few years before 1800 when the great French naturalist Georges Cuvier—then a mere lecturer at the École Centrale du Panthéon and not yet revered as the Father of Paleontology—received a specimen of an Atlantic bird. Cuvier produced a meticulous scientific description of the "type specimen" (the one on which a species is based, usually the first one to be competently described) and named it *Puffinus obscurus*. Just about forty years later, in 1836, John James Audubon painted the bird. The painting became Plate 299 of the so-called Elephant Folio of *Birds of America* with the legend: "Dusky Petrel, Lath., Puffinus Obscurus, Cuvier, Male in Spring, 1836." In the reprint of this book (New York, Macmillan, 1941) the plate number is the same, but the legend gives the name under which the bird is now known: Audubon's shearwater. The scientific name now is *Puffinus Lherminieri*. Audubon's shearwater breeds on various islands, the Bermudas, the Bahamas, and the Lesser Antilles among them. It is a small bird—about a foot long—frequenting the open Atlantic near the American coast. People who have heard its call find it hard to describe but say that the sound resembles the cry of a cat; if written down it comes out as "mee-ow" or "whee-ow."

In 1849 one Mr. J. L. Hurdis visited Bermuda and went to an island—or, better, an islet—called Gurnet Rock. There he found a small sea bird nesting in crevices of the rocks. It was blackish on top and white underneath. It was Cuvier's *Puffinus obscurus,* or the dusky petrel, or Audubon's shearwater. But Mr. Hurdis said that it was also the long-lost cahow. Since it had happened before that the same bird, or mammal, had been given two different names by two different sources and lived a double life (at least in scientific literature) until somebody established identity, a number of writers on Atlantic sea birds or on Bermuda happily accepted the suggestion. Even more than two centuries after its supposed extinction, the shearwater was still rather common.

In 1878 John T. Bartram, who lived on Bermuda and knew the native birds, including Audubon's shearwater, ended the rejoicing by explaining in detail why Mr. Hurdis had to be wrong. The two birds might be similar in appearance, but if you read all the old accounts carefully you had to conclude that the shearwater and the cahow could not be the same bird. The shearwater, Mr. Bartram continued, was the bird called "pimlico" by the early settlers.[1]

After that science was back where it had been, namely to the "extinct Bermuda cahow." Only in one respect had it advanced a little: quite a number of skeletons of the original cahow had been found, in a so-called subfossil state, on a number of the islands.

On February 20, 1906, the story moved another step for-

[1] Fishermen are said still to use this name. Unfortunately the name "pimlico" is also used in Australia for the strong-voiced *Tropidorhynchus corniculatus,* the so-called friar-bird.

ward. The director of the Bermuda Aquarium, Louis L. Mowbray, took a shearwater from a rock crevice on the southeast side of Castle Island. But it was not Audubon's shearwater. It was at least a new subspecies, more likely a new species. The bird was put on record with the provisional name of *Aestrelata gularis*. The specimen was of course preserved, and after a lapse of quite a number of years it occurred to Mr. Mowbray to compare it with the subfossil skeletons of the historic cahow. And in 1916 Louis L. Mowbray and John T. Nichols redescribed the 1906 specimen, as the type specimen of *Pterodroma cahow*!

Since there had been a living cahow in 1906 there was really no reason to assume that there could not be living cahows in 1916. The bird was obviously exceedingly rare, but it just does not happen that there is only one specimen of a species. True, there had been a day when the last quagga died in a zoological garden and another day when the last passenger pigeon died in another zoological garden. But these had been captive specimens which survived under care, while the species outside the zoo walls was known to be extinct. The cahow of 1906 had been caught in the open, which was a different story.

But the chapter "Confusion" in the story of the cahow was not yet finished. In 1932 there came what William Beebe described later as a false alarm on his part. Professor Beebe then had a laboratory on Nonsuch Island, and in the evening he heard bird calls across the water, "a trisyllabic, silvery minor chord: *whee-o! whee-whee-o!*" He finally succeeded in establishing the direction from which the calls seemed to come. It might be Green Island, or else Idol Island, the latter measuring just about 100 feet across. A trip proved that it was not Green Island, so Beebe moved on to Idol Island: "This islet I found the metropolis of these birds. They proved to be Dusky or Audubon Shearwaters." William Beebe told about his experience in chapter ix of his book *Nonsuch, Land of Water,* which was published in New York in 1932. While the text always refers to the birds found on Idol Island as shearwaters, the chapter title is "Cahows and Longtails," and all the pictures of the shearwater are labeled "cahow." The old mistake had been repeated.

But apparently fate itself decided that Dr. Beebe should get out of this with some honor. Early in June of 1935 a bird killed itself flying against the lighthouse on St. David's Island. The lighthouse keeper, a Mr. O'Connor, knew about William Beebe and indulged in the laudable habit of sending him any strange bird that came to grief on the lighthouse on stormy nights. The "dead petrel" reached Dr. Beebe on June 8. "My ornithological library in Bermuda is very limited," he wrote later in the same year, "in comparison with the extended one devoted to fish, and I was unable satisfactorily to identify the bird. So I sent it to Dr. [Robert Cushman] Murphy of the American Museum and excited word came back that it was the second known specimen of the real cahow. . . ."

This was exciting all right, but the news posed another problem for Dr. Beebe:

When I realized the great scientific worth of the specimen my mind went back to the skeleton. Mr. Tee-Van had skinned the bird for me, and had no recollection of what he had done with the body. As I thought at that time it was some well-known species, I had felt no concern about saving the trunk bones. About a month after this we were getting a wicker fish trap ready for use when I noticed a small cluster of well-cleaned bones inside. My artist, Mr. Swanson, saw them at the same moment, and exclaimed that they must be those of the cahow, as he recalled, a month before, throwing the fresh body of the petrel into the trap with other bait and then dropping the whole overboard. Examination showed the entire trunk, vertebrae, furcula and breast-bone to be intact and beautifully cleaned by fish and water. So the only known recent skeleton of this species was retrieved.

By that time it was certain that the cahow was not extinct. Now the major duty of everybody concerned or even interested was to be sure it did not become extinct at this late date. But it had to be found first.

A "field investigation"—islet investigation in this case—was called for.

The Second World War delayed things a bit. But it also brought additional evidence. An American Army officer, Fred T. Hall, stationed on Bermuda in 1945, spent his leisure time looking for cahows. He found one on the beach, the partly decayed body of an adult cahow that had drifted ashore. On land he found fragments of birds which apparently had been killed and eaten by rats.

After the war Dr. Murphy began to think about a field investigation in earnest. The man he approached with the idea was Mr. Childs Frick, who was one of the trustees of the museum, and, moreover, owned a home in Bermuda. After Mr. Frick had promised his assistance in more than one way, Dr. Murphy got in touch with the curator of the Bermuda Aquarium, Louis S. Mowbray, the son of the man who discovered the 1906 specimen.

Some of the historic breeding grounds of the cahow were obviously "impossible" for the bird in January 1951 when the field party flew to Bermuda. Castle Island is now frequently visited by tourists for the sake of the old fortifications there. Cooper's Island has been linked with St. David's Island by filling and is part of the Bermuda Air Base. Gurnet Rock, which was promising, could not be investigated because the winter seas made a landing impossible. A number of promising islets (probably around Cooper's Island) were examined, and on January 28, 1951, the party went to "Islet A." Under a rocky ledge a tunnel was found and a flashlight revealed a bird in the nesting chamber, presumably sitting on an egg.

"With a noose at the end of a bamboo we succeeded in hauling out the bird," Dr. Murphy reported (in *Natural History*, April 1951). "There was a breathless moment before daylight showed it to be the longed-for but only half-anticipated cahow! Its egg could then be seen in the nest. Our almost unbelievable captive bit the hands that grasped it but only half-heartedly. Within a moment it became completely unresistant, allowing itself to be stroked, tickled and passed from hand to hand. We banded and photographed it

The Bermuda cahow

and jotted down hasty descriptions of its flesh colors, including the pink feet. When put on the ground, it scurried back to its egg. During the whole period of badgering, extraction and handling, it had neither uttered a sound nor ejected oil from the throat or nostrils. The last point is noteworthy. No cahow handled during our visit spewed out stomach oil in the reaction that is so common among petrels. All the birds remained docile, dry and fluffy, as well as practically devoid of odor."

Since the cahow is nocturnal, there followed a night watch on a rocky islet beaten by the waves. To add to the discomfort it began to rain. In spite of all their scientific zeal the people could easily imagine more friendly surroundings, but the cahows were undisturbed. Several of

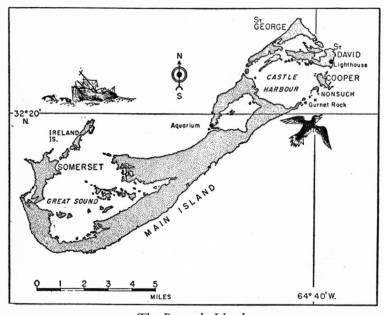

The Bermuda Islands

The breeding places of the cahow are at the eastern end of the group

them were seen, and in one nest a pair of cahows carried on what ornithologists call "connubial posturing and display" for three hours without paying any attention to the flashlight beam thrown at them at intervals.

The result of the whole investigation was that a hundred cahows were estimated to be living on a number of islets.

The government of Bermuda responded immediately by declaring all these islets sanctuaries.

The next step to be taken was a local war against rats. Rats, of course, are the enemies of all ground-nesting birds, but long watches in front of cahow burrows proved that the cahow alone has another enemy whom no naturalist had even suspected. This enemy is the long-tailed tropic bird, well known as one of the bird species breeding on Bermuda. What happens, according to the American conservationist Richard Thorsell, who helped Louis S. Mowbray stand watch, is that the tropic birds arrive at a time when the cahow has hatched its single egg and the nest is inhabited by a defenseless young bird. The tropic birds prefer an existing burrow to the work of tunneling their own; they do away with the young cahow and take over the nest.

Mr. Thorsell thinks that he has found a defense. He has built wooden baffles to be placed over the tunnel entrances, with openings large enough for a cahow to get through, but too small for a tropic bird. These should help—but after all the cahow did manage by itself to survive through centuries when nobody knew that it even existed.

10: The Waldrapp
of Switzerland

THINGS Swiss, provided that they also have something to do with natural history, are almost invariably connected with the name of Konrad Gesner.

It is true that only specialists know that Konrad Gesner was born in Zürich on March 26, 1516, as one of the numerous (but totally unfamous and forgotten) children of the furrier Urs Gesner, and that his first position after his student days was that of professor of Greek at Lausanne. A few men of letters or Latin scholars may know of his *Bibliotheca universalis,* a bibliography of all authors who wrote in Latin, Hebrew, or Greek up to Gesner's time; it appeared in 1545, except for the never-finished part that was to be devoted to medical literature. Linguists may know, at least by reputation, one of Gesner's books, *Mithridates, sive de differentiis linguarum* (1555), in which he tried to establish the relationship of the various languages to one another, using the Lord's Prayer as a recurrent example for each. But only a Swiss historian would know that Gesner was dissatisfied with Dr. Martinus Luther's translation of the Lord's Prayer and made one of his own which was used in the churches of Zürich in his time.

To the large majority of people who know about Konrad Gesner at all, he was the man who, while municipal physician of Zürich, wrote the enormous *Historia animalium,* the big compendium of zoological knowledge (and lore) which present-day zoologists consider the beginning of their science, and which contained, in five enormous folio volumes, everything known at the time about animals. The first of these volumes, treating the mammals, appeared in 1551; the fourth, about the fishes, in 1558; while a fifth, incomplete and fragmentary and dealing with the "serpents" (meaning reptiles), was printed in 1587, twenty-two years after Gesner succumbed to the pulmonary form of the bubonic plague.

The purpose of Gesner's work was, of course, to collect all available information and to clarify it. Zoologists who came after him used the work—especially the almost contemporary German edition—to good purpose for centuries, and only rarely did they have to mark sections as points where Gesner had been misled by his correspondents, or as points where Gesner should have said, "This might be literary tradition but it is *not* zoology," more loudly than he did say it.

Only if one knows these facts can one understand why a questionable chapter bothered later zoologists as much as it did. This chapter occurs in the third volume, the one devoted to birds, which was published for the first time in 1555, and begins on page 337 of the original Latin edition. The chapter heading is *"De Corvo Sylvatico,"* meaning "Of the Wood (or Forest) Raven." In the first German edition the chapter begins on page 199, under the heading *"Von dem Waldrappen,"* which, of course, means the same thing. *Wald* is the German word for forest and *Rapp* (in modern German *Rabe*) means raven, though popular usage did not always draw as clear a distinction between ravens and crows as is customary in English. The chapter begins with the sentence: "The bird shown in the illustration is usually called by our people [the Swiss] *ein Waldrapp* because its habitat is unpeopled forests where it lives on high cliffs and sometimes on old ruins, which has led to the name of *Steinrapp* (stone

raven), and elsewhere, as in Bavaria and Styria, it is called
ein Klaussrapp because of the narrow openings [in German:
Klause] in the rock where he builds his nest. In Lothringia
and near the Paffyer Lake they call him *Meerrapp* [sea
raven]."

All this sounds as commonplace as possible. Gesner did
not, as elsewhere, quote from classical authors or from the
statements of recent travelers; he was obviously writing
about something he knew himself. If our ring-necked pheas-
ant or cardinal had a number of different names somebody
living in upstate New York might well begin a description
of one of these birds in just such a manner. Gesner then goes
on to say that the hunters consider the Waldrapp especially
tasty and that they manage to obtain the young birds, just
before they can fly, by descending, well secured with ropes,
to the nests from a higher vantage point.

He backtracks to names for a second to say, "Because of
its call the bird is also called a *Scheller*." The latter word is
hard to translate; it is related to *Schelle,* which means a
small and unharmonious or strident bell. Apparently the
call of the Waldrapp was nothing to praise.

Then he proceeds to the unspoken question of what kind
of bird it is: "Turnerus" (the Englishman Turner) believes
that the 'water raven' of Aristotle and the Phalacrocorax
of Pliny and our Waldrapp is one and the same bird, but
wrongly, since he does not resemble the descriptions of these
birds, does not have webbed feet, and is no water fowl but
looks for his food in green gardens. . . ." A direct description follows: "Our Waldrapp is of the size of a hen, completely black if you see him at a distance, but if you have
him close by to look at, especially if the sun be behind him,
he seems to be tinged with green. His feet are not quite like
those of chicken, but longer. . . ."

Further definite information, all obviously derived from
personal experience, follows without any pause. The tail
feathers are short, and "he grows bald-headed with age as I

have seen." On the back of the head there is a "small bouquet" of feathers, pointing backward: "I don't know whether all have them and all year round."

"The beak is reddish and long and good for digging into the soil and for thrusting into narrow cracks of rocks or walls to pull out worms and beetles. He has long red legs. They

DE CORVO SYLVATICO.

A v i s, cuius hic effigies habetur, à noſtris nominatur uulgo ein Wldrapp, id eſt coruus ſyluaticus, quòd locis ſyluoſis, montanis & deſertis degere ſoleat:ubi in rupibus, aut turribus deſertis nidificat. quare etiam Steintrapp uocatur, & alibi (in Bauaria & Stiria) ein Clauſtrapp: à petris ſeu rupibus, & pylis (nam pylas, id eſt anguſtias inter duos montes Germani clauſen appellant, hoc eſt loca clauſa) in quibus nidos ſtruit. Lotharingi, ut audio, corneille de mer, id eſt cornix marina: quam et in ſuglandibus aliquando nidificare ferunt, ſed forte ea alia auis eſt. Circa lacum Verbanum coruus marinus dicitur. alibi in Italia coruus ſyluaticus, ut in Iſtria circa promontorium Polæ, ubi homine per ſunem demiſſo per rupes nidis eximuntur, & inter menſarum delicias habentur, ut apud nos quoqʒ in montium quorundam rupibus, ſic enim Fabarias thermas repertas aiunt, cum auceps quidam per altiſsimas rupes propter has aues ſe demiſiſſet. Alibi in Italia coruo ſpilato , id eſt coruus depilis, quoniam ſeneſcens calueſcat. Germanicè quidam nuper confiſto à ſe à ſono uocis eius nomine Scheller uocabat. ¶ Sunt qui phala-

Konrad Gesner's Waldrapp; reproduction of a page from the original Latin edition of Konrad Gesner's *Historia animalium*, volume III [the birds] eat grasshoppers, crickets, small fish and young frogs . . . when I cut open the stomach of this bird I found large numbers of those insects which harm the roots of plants, especially millet. They also eat the worms which develop into May beetles. These birds are the first of all migratory birds to fly away, around the begining of June."

Gesner adds that they fly especially high, that the nest contains two or three eggs, and that young birds taken from the nest before they can fly will become tame, fly out into the fields to forage, and then return to the house. The last sentences of the chapter—I give them practically in full—read: "The young ones are highly esteemed for food and considered a special treat, for they have lovely flesh and soft bones. Those who take them from their nests always leave one in each nest so that the bird will return again in the following year."

I repeat, the whole was obviously written from close personal observation, a description of a reasonably large, insect-eating, migratory bird. It was just this simple matter-of-factness that baffled later zoologists, around, say, 1700. Because, as far as their knowledge went, *there was no such bird as the Waldrapp!*

Naturally a search was made through libraries, through books written by others in Gesner's time and soon after. The findings were carefully tabulated. There was a bird—obviously the same one—called *Phalacrocorax ex Illyrio missus* by the Italian Ulisse Aldrovandi in *Ornithologia*, III, 1603, page 267. In a British work, Francis Willughby's *Ornithology* of 1678, on page 396, there appeared a bird called "Gesner's Wood-Crow," indubitably the Waldrapp. Another Englishman, Eleazar Albin, who wrote a *Natural History of Birds* around 1740, listed "the Wood-Crow from Switzerland," and even, on plate 18, gave a picture "from the collection of Sir Th. Lowther." Add to this a chance mention of the bird in the "Swiss Chronicles" by Johannes Stumpf, both compatriot and contemporary of Gesner, where it is referred to as a "common fowl," and that completed the list.

All this was very fine, but it was also an established fact that no European zoologist of the early eighteenth century had ever seen a Waldrapp. Actually there might be just one source, namely Gesner, for the story of its existence. The Englishmen had not written from personal observation; their references had been based on Gesner's work. As for Aldrovandi, his might be based on Gesner too, one couldn't be sure. Stumpf had not made a special point of describing the bird: he might have meant something else.

When Karl von Linné (Carolus Linnaeus) in Sweden evolved his "natural system" of the animals and had progressed to the birds in about 1758, Gesner's Waldrapp was already a minor puzzle. Linné did not know this bird from personal observation. There were no specimens in the collections accessible to him. But Gesner's description could not just be pushed aside. And even though both Ray, who wrote the portion of Willughby's work in which the Waldrapp appears, and Albin, might have had no source other than Gesner, plate 18 in Albin's book was based not on Gesner's *liber tertius* but on a stuffed specimen. At least that's what the book said. Linné did not have too much material to go by, but the curved beak which was evident in the pictures, and the tuft on the head, reminded him of the hoopoe. Consequently after the hoopoe *(Upupa epops)*, which he did know —it ranges from southern Sweden to southern Europe and points east—Linné listed the hermit hoopoe, labeled *Upupa eremita,* putting it under the genus *Corvus,* alongside the raven and various crows. But he still had to use the same old descriptions; no new specimen that could be investigated carefully and at leisure had come to light. When, half a century after Linné, there still was no new specimen, ornithologists began to grow exceedingly suspicious. Notwithstanding Gesner's fame and his undoubted honesty, there existed the possibility that he had made a mistake.

The first man to suggest this was the German zoologist and forester Johann Matthäus Bechstein. But even he moved slowly. When he wrote a book with a title that might be translated as *General Natural History of Germany,* he still mentioned the Waldrapp and printed an old picture of it (source unknown). The first edition of Bechstein's book appeared in 1791. In 1805, there was a second edition, and in it Bechstein stated that Gesner probably had meant to describe the bird which in more recent works was named *Pyrrhocorax graculus,* commonly called the "red-billed alpine crow." What Gesner had said about the one did not fit the other perfectly, but it came close. The alpine crow has coral-red legs and a curved bill of the same color. Its plumage is black, with a greenish or bluish sheen. Both beak and legs seemed to be considerably shorter than shown in Gesner's illustration, but who could trust an artist of that period to be faithful in rendering detail? The alpine crow was smaller than Gesner had described his Waldrapp, and the alpine crow as a rule lays four or five eggs. But such deviations seemed comparatively small. That the alpine crow does not have a tuft of feathers on the back of the head and does not grow bald-headed with age was somewhat awkward, but Gesner himself had made a minor question mark about just these facts. His most positive assertions had been about the diet and the dissection of the stomach, and that diet agreed generally with the known diet of the alpine crow. Finally, while the alpine crow is not rare, it does happen to be rare in the Swiss Alps, which presumably was true in Gesner's time too.

This explanation was by no means perfect, but it was better by far than no explanation at all. Hence it was concluded that Gesner, in describing *Corvus sylvaticus,* had really meant *Pyrrhocorax graculus.* If anybody had ever sat down and compiled a careful list of all the "mistakes" Gesner made if he had really been describing *Pyrrhocorax,* the explanation would have been found to be dubious, to say the least. But nobody did.

Bechstein did have a rather strong case; all the circumstantial evidence was on his side. To begin with, Gesner's chapter looked like the *only* primary source. More important, this was not a purely literary problem of establishing who said what first. It had to do with the alleged existence of a reasonably conspicuous item of natural history. And there was no Waldrapp.

No matter how others may have felt, they could do nothing but give in. The Waldrapp was a closed, though not completely explained, case.

Things remained that way, or seemed to, for almost a century—for 92 years, to be precise about it. In 1897 three gentlemen met more or less accidentally in the library of a zoological museum, the Rothschild Museum in Tring in Hertfordshire, not far from London. They were Lionel Walter, second Baron de Rothschild and Member of Parliament (present in his capacity as an enthusiastic zoologist), Otto Kleinschmidt, a German Protestant theologian and well-reputed ornithologist, and Ernst Johann Otto Hartert, a German naturalist and co-editor of the professional journal *Novitates zoologicae*. Their discussion is said to have begun with a chance remark about a minor though amusing mistake made by Henry E. Dresser.

Dresser, after many years of preparation, had published a work entitled *History of the Birds of Europe* (1880). It was a grandiose and fine and reliable book. But, as title page and preface proclaimed, it was a book about the birds of Europe, and for no reason that anybody could explain, Dresser had included an ibis in volume VI. It was the species of ibis which bore the scientific name *Geronticus comatus*—also called *Ibis comata*—and which had been discovered by Wagler in Egypt in 1832. Soon after, several other travelers had reported the same ibis from Syria, Arabia, and Abyssinia. Egypt, as every schoolboy knows, is the classical land of the ibis. These discoveries had merely added another species of ibis in the same corner of the world, northeast Africa and adjacent territories.

The *Geronticus* could at best be called a "British colonial," not a European, and did not belong in the book at all. Incidentally, did anybody know whether Wagler derived its name from the Latin or from the Greek? If from the Latin, the root word was *gero,* meaning to carry; the second half of the name, *comatus,* came from the Latin too, from *coma* for "hair," referring in this case to the thatch of feathers. But it could just as well be Greek, coming from *geron,* "an old

The crested ibis, *Comatibis eremita,* of Asia Minor, Arabia, and Abyssinia, which was once a migratory bird

man." The wrinkled skin of the bird's head and face could easily suggest an old man, especially since the bird looked so bald-headed!

"... grows bald-headed in his old age, as I have seen. ...."

Books were hauled off the shelves: Gesner, volume III; Albin; Bechstein's first edition; Dresser. The first three contained three different old pictures, all purporting to show the "mythical" Waldrapp. In Dresser's book there was a picture of the well-established ibis *Geronticus* from Egypt and vicinity. No doubt about it, it was the same bird. Bechstein had said, "There is no such bird in Europe"; he should have said, "There is no longer such a bird in Europe." The three men sat down together and wrote an article which Hartert published in *Novitates zoologicae*, volume IV, 1897, page 371. The title, restoring a previously used name, read: "*Comatibis eremita*, a European Bird"—vindicating Dresser's accidental inclusion of it in his volume and vindicating Gesner too.

After Rothschild, Kleinschmidt, and Hartert had successfully demolished one of Bechstein's two tenets—namely, that the bird itself did not exist—a German zoologist and historian, Robert Lauterborn, went ahead to ruin Bechstein's other assertion. Gesner's chapter was the only independent source on the Waldrapp? That remained to be seen! And Lauterborn succeeded in turning up numerous entries in chronicles of the period from 1500 to shortly after 1600 which made it possible to establish where the Waldrapp had lived in Europe. Switzerland had not been the center of its original habitat but one of the flanks. It lived in northern Italy, Switzerland, Bavaria, Styria, and "Illyria"—modern Dalmatia, Bosnia and Herzegovina, parts of western Serbia and Montenegro.[1]

But Switzerland not only provided the best and for a long time the only literary source; it was found later to have also provided the earliest literary source. In the *Natural History* of Pliny the Elder, dating from the first century A.D., there is a short note which can only refer to the Waldrapp. It can be found in Book x, Chapter 68. In Pliny's time Egnatius Calvinus was the Roman prefect "in the Alps," and he wrote back to Rome that he had seen ibises there—"a bird which is peculiar to Egypt." To the widely traveled Roman, the Waldrapp looked like an ibis; the Swiss of the sixteenth

---

[1] The present distribution is Asia Minor, Syria, Palestine, Arabia, and Abyssinia; Egypt, where Wagler discovered it, does not seem to harbor it any more.

century, who did not move far from the place where they were born, compared it to the raven.

Interestingly enough, Gesner himself had noticed the similarity with the ibis; in the ibis chapter of his book he wrote: "A bird can be found in the Alps which is called a 'black stork,' but which cannot be called an ibis because of its straight bill, just as the Waldrapp cannot be the 'black ibis' even though it has a curved bill because it does not resemble the ibis in other ways." Well, Gesner was wrong there; the Waldrapp is an ibis and for some time it was the only European ibis.

We don't know just when it stopped being a European bird; in other words, when it stopped being migratory. Lauterborn did not find any references after, say, 1620. So the bird stopped migrating to Europe—or at least to the Bavarian, Austrian, and Swiss areas; we don't know about the west Balkan coast—around the middle of the seventeenth century.

The remaining question is: Why?

11: The Furry Old Man of the Sea

ON JULY 7, 1911, four great powers signed an international treaty which is remarkable on three counts. The first is that it has been faithfully kept ever since, even while some of the treaty makers were at war with each other. The second is that it accomplished its purpose. And the third is that many statesmen and probably all professional historians do not even know that it exists.

The signatories to the treaty were, reading clockwise around the northern Pacific Ocean: the Empire of Japan, the Empire of Russia, the United States of America, and the British Empire. The reason for this sequence is that the treaty had to do with the protection of an animal which occurred along the shores of the northern Pacific. The habitat of the animal in question began near the northeastern capes of the Japanese island of Hokkaido, extended along the Chishima or Kurile islands, the Komandorskie islands, along the chain of the Aleutians, and southward along the coasts of Alaska and British Columbia and the Pacific coast of the United States, all the way down to Baja California. The animal protected by the treaty was the sea otter *Enhydra lutris* (in older books it usually appears as *Latax lutris*), the only one of the otter-like animals which has adapted itself to life in salt water.

The sea otter is also the largest of the otter-like animals. A fully grown specimen will measure about 5 feet and weigh as much as 80 pounds. To somebody who thinks of an otter as a kind of water weasel this sounds positively gigantic, but the giant river otter of Brazil—the ariranha of the Brazilians and *Pteronura brasiliensis* of the zoologists—is not much smaller though a good deal lighter. And the Canadian otter, *Lutra canadensis,* does not lag far behind the Brazilian giant otter in size. In build the sea otter is rather on the massive side as far as its body is concerned, at least for an otter. The head with its grumpy-looking face is comparatively small, the forepaws are tiny but agile (dexterous would be an even better term if it could be extended to both paws), and the tail is short and somewhat flattened. The hind paws of the sea otter, comparable in size to a man's hand, have a strangely triangular shape, caused by the fact that the length of the digits increases from the inside out. They are very flat, flipper-like, and extremely flexible. While superlative in their function when in water, they are poor means of loco-motion on land. For some reason the animal is incapable of putting them down flat—the toes double under so that it walks, or rather hops, on the backs of its feet. Especially on a rocky beach this makes progress slow and actually painful. A sea otter which has been chased for some distance on land will have lacerated and bleeding hind feet.

There are two subspecies, probably just two races, of the sea otter. The animal that occurred from Hokkaido, via the Bering Sea, to British Columbia, Vancouver Island, and the state of Washington was one species. Along the Oregon shore it seems to have always been rare. One expert blamed this fact on Oregon's sandy beaches, since the sea otter is known to prefer rocky coasts and islands, but the reason may simply be that there was less food along that stretch of the coast. In California the sea otter was again common, but there it was the subspecies or race called the southern sea otter. The only definite difference between the two types seems to lie in some of the bones of the skull; it has been stated that headless corpses of the two subspecies could not be told apart. The fur of the southern sea otter seems to be always brown, while the northern sea otter tends to darker shades, but even in the north very dark brown or black animals are in the minority.

One very surprising fact about the sea otter's fur is that it hangs loosely on the animal; a sea-otter skin when stretched out on a frame for drying looks much larger than the animal from which it was taken. On the frame it may measure 90 inches in length and 36 inches in width; this, of course, is a skin from a fully grown specimen. The fur has a very fine, silky texture, with the individual hairs between 1 and 1½ inches in length, and suggests both warmth and luxury. When the Indians of Vancouver Island were made acquainted with silk velvet they promptly gave it the same name they use for sea-otter fur.

And with the fur of the sea otter we have arrived at the core of a story the unpleasantness of which is ameliorated only by a reasonably happy ending. The story of the sea otter is actually the story of its fur. Though the most diversified kinds of people have, on one occasion or another, eaten sea-otter meat their opinion about it was usually such that the sea otter's existence would never have been endangered for that reason. It was the fur which caused it to be hunted into near-extinction; the sea otter is now alive only because of the treaty of 1911 and a fortunate change in fashion trends.

Of course a few sea otters were clubbed or speared to death for food by tribesmen along the animal's 6000-mile range at various times during the unrecorded history of these tribes. Sea-otter bones have been found in Indian shell heaps on various islands off Baja California. Whether the Indians who killed and ate them made any use of the skins is not known; there was no climatic necessity for doing so. It was on one of these islands, Cedros Island, that the Spaniards made the acquaintance of the sea otter in 1733; it may have been for the first time. Señor Miguel Venegas, who kept the diary of the trip made by Padre Sigismundo Taraval, recorded that "they found such numbers of them together that the seamen killed about twenty of them, following them only with sticks. Some of the skins of these creatures the Padre sent to Mexico." Apparently the authorities in Mexico found the skins of commercial value, because at a later date the Spaniards employed Californian Indians to hunt sea otters, paying them 3 to 4 *reales* per skin.

At the same time, but at the other end of the sea-otter's long-extended habitat, the inhabitants of the Kurile Islands hunted too. But in the case of these Ainu—the "hairy Ainu," as they were often called—there was a decided climatic necessity for making use of the skin. The beautiful furs worn by these people gradually became known to both the Japanese and the Russians. The Japanese sold what they could barter —and sometimes steal—in China, where every mandarin insisted on owning a number of fur-trimmed robes. And for some time one specific Japanese lord had a monopoly on the trade in sea-otter skins, a monopoly that was strictly enforced by death sentences when necessary. The actual hunting seems to have been done by the Ainu, with the Japanese acting merely as traders. The Russians did their own hunting.

It was due to the Russians that a fine scientific description of the sea otter was written around the middle of the eighteenth century. The situation along the northeastern coast of Asia was muddled at that time. The Japanese infiltrated on Sakhalin Island and the Russians infiltrated on the Kurile Islands. The Kamchatka peninsula was in Russian hands, or, to put it more precisely, there were Russians on Kamchatka. But no one was quite sure whether this peninsula wasn't an island, and whether the eastern tip of Asia and the western tip of America were separated by sea or not was anybody's guess.

Czar Peter the Great had been sufficiently imbued with

Western ideas while living among the Dutch to decide not just to believe what he liked best but to send somebody to find out the facts. His choice fell on a Dane, Vitus Jonassen Bering, who in turn picked a German, Georg Wilhelm Steller, to accompany his expedition as a naturalist. The expedition was known in its time as the trans-Asiatic expedition, for it had been decided to take an overland route to the Far East.

The second of Bering's expeditions actually reached America, namely Alaska, at a time when the weather was bad and Bering was at the end of his endurance. Much against Steller's wishes he ordered the return trip almost immediately, and, as is well known, his ship was wrecked on the island which now bears his name. Bering died there; his naturalist made several discoveries. In addition to some known seals and foxes there were strange marine mammals on the shore of that cold island. Steller discovered and described the animal which his Russian companions called *morskaya korova,* meaning "sea cow"—a relative of the manatee, now called Steller's sea cow.[1] There was also an animal which the Russians called *morskoy bobr* or "sea beaver"; it was the sea otter.

Steller knew, of course, that the animal was not a beaver but an otter. He observed correctly that only one young was born at a time, as one would expect of a mammal with only two teats. Strangely enough, he mentioned a "mating period," though all later observers are agreed that the young can be born at any time of the year. Probably he observed several matings at the time he was on Bering Island and drew the logical conclusion that this was the mating period. He also noticed that the food of the sea otter consisted of "marine crustaceans, mollusks, small fishes, a little seaweed"; in American waters, at least, the favorite food of the animal is sea urchins. Whether the very small amounts of kelp that

[1] See *The Lungfish, the Dodo, and the Unicorn,* Chapter 14.

were found in the stomachs of killed animals had been eaten purposely or just "went along" with the overwhelmingly carnivorous diet is uncertain.

Steller is the only man to my knowledge to say that "the meat is fairly good to eat and palatable; the females, however, are much tenderer. . . . The suckling otters which, because of their poor skin, are called *medvyedki* or young bears, can, because of their daintiness, both roasted and boiled, at any time compete with suckling lambs." Since the survivors of Bering's expedition subsisted for a long time

The sea otter

on seal, sea cow, and sea otter, it is quite logical to assume that Steller's taste buds had become inured to meat with a violently fishy taste. Besides, he was grateful to the sea otter: "This animal deserves from us all the greatest reverence, as for more than six months it served us almost exclusively as food and at the same time as medicine for the scurvy-stricken."

"Altogether," wrote Steller, "in life it is a beautiful and pleasing animal, cunning and amusing in its habits, and at the same time ingratiating and amorous. Seen when they are running, the gloss of their hair surpasses the blackest velvet.

They prefer to lie together in families, the male with its mate, the half-grown young, or *koshloki,* and the very young sucklings, *medvyedki.* The male caresses the female by stroking her, using the forefeet as hands, and places himself over her; she, however, often pushes him away from her for fun and in simulated coyness . . . and plays with her offspring like the fondest mother. . . . In flight they take the suckling young in the mouth, but the grown-up [young] ones they drive before them. If they have the luck to escape they begin, as soon as they are in the water, to mock their pursuers in such a manner that one cannot look on without particular pleasure. Now they stand upright in the water like a man and jump up and down with the waves and sometimes hold the forefoot over the eyes and look at you as if the sun troubled them, now they throw themselves on their back and with the front feet rub the belly and the pudenda as do monkeys; then they throw the young ones into the water and catch them again. . . . When dead it lies like a dead person, with the front feet crossed over the breast."

Some trade values for the pelts were established even in Steller's time, for he noted that "the best pelts bring in Kamchatka 20 rubles, in Yakutsk 30, in Irkutsk 40 to 50, and at the Chinese frontier, in exchange for their wares, 80 to 100 rubles." Though the men of Bering's expedition hunted essentially for food they were aware of the market value of the pelts: "From November 6, 1741, to August 17, 1742 over 700 otters were killed by us, eaten, and their skins taken along to Kamchatka as tokens." The landing of the "lost" expedition at Kamchatka caused quite a sensation, partly because everybody had ceased to expect its return, but largely because of the more than 700 "tokens" they brought with them. The Russians, the traditional fur hunters and fur traders of the last five centuries, looked at the bounty and plans began to form in their minds. They probably did not know, and most certainly did not care, what the expedition of "Ivan Ivanovitch" (as they called

Bering for no other reason than that it sounded familiar to them) had been supposed to accomplish. What it had proved was that there were islands out there where fur-bearing animals were plentiful.

One of those who went to look for these islands was a shipmate of Bering and Steller, Mikhail Novodchikov, who was the first to set foot on the westernmost of the Aleutian Islands. Others followed. One Andrei Tolstyk reported that in three trips into the still-uncharted island chain, made in 1749, 1756, and 1760, he took the skins of 9397 adult otters and of 821 cubs. In 1783 one Gregory Shelekhov established a Russian fur-trading outpost in Alaska. It was the beginning of the Russian America Company, which was a most profitable venture until about 1860.

In the meantime something else had happened, curiously enough also as the result of a scientific expedition. On his last voyage of exploration Captain James Cook reached Vancouver Island and dropped anchor in Nootka Sound. What happened there was described by an American who was on board, John Ledyard: "We purchased [from the Indians] while here [Nootka Sound] about 1500 beaver, besides other skins, but took none but the best, having no thoughts at the time of using them to any other advantage than to the purpose of cloathing." The "beaver" which were bought for "cloathing" were, of course, sea otter; Ledyard used the Russian term that he learned later. Captain Cook met his death on that last voyage and the new commander decided to sail for England along the shortest possible route. Like Steller some four decades earlier, he landed at Petropavlovsk, and the Russian fur traders saw what he had on board. In Mr. Ledyard's words: "It afterwards happened that skins which did not cost the purchaser sixpence sterling sold in China for 100 dollars." Among them the sailors of Captain Cook's ship realized $10,000 on the skins they had bought on Vancouver Island.

Shortly after the publication, in 1784, of Cook's account of his last voyage the English traders began to come to Vancouver Island in search of the valuable furs he had described. Captain James Hanna arrived in 1785. He gathered 560 skins which he sold at Canton for $20,600. Next year he sailed again from Macao, but this time he was less successful, returning with only 100 skins, valued at $8000. In 1785 James Strange organized an expedition of two ships commanded by Captains Laurie and Guise. They sailed from Bombay to Nootka and cruised in Prince William Sound during 1786. Their catch was only 604 skins, worth $24,000. Captain John Meares came in the *Nootka* in 1786 from Calcutta to Prince William Sound. He obtained 50 otter skins that sold for $91 each, as well as 267 other furs worth from $5 to $70 apiece. Captain Charles William Barkley, in the *Imperial Eagle,* arrived on the coast at about the same time and collected 800 skins of superior quality. His cargo brought $30,000 at Canton. In 1787 Captain George Dixon in the *Queen Charlotte* and Captain Nathaniel Portlock in the *King George,* working together, did a good business in furs along the coast. . . . They collected 2552 otter skins, which were sold for $54,857.

Then came the Boston traders, for most of the American ships that voyaged to the Northwest Coast in those days sailed from Boston. In 1801 fifteen such ships arrived; and in 1802 more than 15,000 otter skins were obtained and taken to Canton. It is probable that the Russians collected 10,000 similar skins in the same year, so that the aggregate for the season was at least 25,000. Captain John Suter in the *Pearl* in two seasons, 1808 and 1809, obtained 6000 skins.[2]

Russians, Englishmen, and Americans were engaged in a wild race to grow rich on fur, at the expense of the fast-diminishing population of harmless sea otters. The head of the Russian America Company in Alaska was one Alexander Baranov, who must have been an extraordinary character in many respects, though one would wish that he had made a career of finding ores rather than of killing animals.

[2] "The Sea-Otter in History," by T. A. Rickard, in *The British Columbia Historical Quarterly,* vol. XI, January 1947.

He made deals with American captains and bought most of his provisions from Boston, which was much closer to him than Russia proper. In 1809 John Jacob Astor sent his *Enterprise* to Baranov, loaded with supplies which included 419 gallons of gin, 684 gallons of rum, and 908 gallons of brandy—it is, as everybody knows, quite cold up there. Baranov bought $26,883.92 worth of supplies for which he paid in sealskins, sea-otter pelts, and beaver furs.

Many of the hunters employed by Baranov were not Russians but Aleutians, though the ships carrying the Aleutian hunters and their kayak-like *bidarkas* were manned by Russians, and sometimes by Americans. The Russians ranged down the American west coast in pursuit of the sea otter and even entered San Francisco Bay, to the intense annoyance of the Mexicans, who lacked fighting ships to prevent them or to chase them out.

One might say that the sea otter was ultimately saved because the Russians thought of themselves too much as overlords of everything they surveyed. In 1821 the Czar issued an *ukas* prohibiting non-Russian ships from entering the Bering Sea or approaching the coast of the Russian possessions in America. Great Britain and the United States protested immediately, and in 1824 and 1825 treaties were signed which established international rights and relations between the three powers. The charter of the Russian America Company, which had been extended and extended again several times over, finally expired on December 31, 1861, and Prince Maksutov was appointed Imperial Governor of Russian America. By that time the suggestion that the United States simply buy the whole territory from the Russians had already been made; the delays which followed are directly attributable to the Civil War. The treaty for the purchase was signed March 30, 1867, the price was $7,200,000, and the territory was formally transferred to the United States on October 18, 1867, at Sitka, a city founded by Alexander Baranov.

American ownership expressed itself in something not known in Russian times—a comprehensive survey of what had been bought, and, moreover, a survey that was published. It was House Exec. Doc. 83, 44th Congress, 1st Session, entitled *A Report upon the Condition of Affairs in the Territory of Alaska,* written by Henry Wood Elliott and published in 1875. In the chapter devoted to the sea otter (still treated as a natural resource rather than a natural curiosity), Elliott wrote: "The Russians were taking between 400 and 500 sea-otters from the Aleutian Islands and south of the Peninsula of Alaska, with perhaps 150 more from Kenai, Yahkutat, and the Sitkan district; the Hudson's Bay Company and other traders getting about 200 more from the coast of Queen Charlotte's and Vancouver's Islands, and off Gray's Harbor, Washington Territory. Now, during the last season, 1873, instead of less than 700 skins, as obtained by the Russians, our traders secured not much less than 4000 skins. This immense difference is not due to the fact of there being a proportionate increase of sea-otters, but to the organization of hunting parties in the spirit and fashion as in the old days." Elliott ended on a note of warning: "The keen competition of our traders will ruin the business in a comparatively short time if some action is not taken by the Government."

Government action was not forthcoming immediately; and there may have been considerable doubt as to just what action should be recommended and taken. It must be remembered that the arctic winter produced a kind of natural closed season on sea otter; in fact the sea otter would not have lasted until 1875 if it had not been for the arctic winter. Besides, the natives of the Aleutian Islands depended on sea otter, a point which is stressed in *A Report on the*

Sea Otter Banks of Alaska, made in 1897 by Captain C. L. Hooper, the commander of the Bering Sea Patrol Fleet.

Captain Hooper provided statistics[3] which proved that the sea-otter population was declining rapidly—reading his figures now, in retrospect, one marvels rather at how large it still was then—and made some recommendations which had the effect of permitting the natives to hunt in their accustomed manner but stopped more commercial exploitation.

By the beginning of the present century it was too late for measures aimed at preserving the sea otter as a natural resource. If it was to be preserved at all it had to be protected completely. In 1910 a law was passed which forbade the killing of sea otters in waters under the jurisdiction of the United States. One year later there followed the international four-power treaty for the preservation of *Enhydra lutris.* Neither Russia nor Japan stopped all hunting in their respective territories. The Russians permitted the taking of a small number every year from one of their islands; the Japanese seem to have established the permissible number every year, with a number of years when the permissible number was zero.

The existence of the treaty and the subsequent restrictions impressed the fur traders as a proof that the animal was decidedly rare. It may even have been a kind of notification

---

[3] "Approximate number of sea otters taken in Alaskan waters by Aleutian Island natives":

1873	2262	1885	4152
1874	2436	1886	3604
1875	2674	1887	3095
1876	2786	1888	2496
1877	2624	1889	1795
1878	2989	1890	1633
1879	3121	1891	1436
1880	3014	1892	820
1881	2999	1893	686
1882	3114	1894	598
1883	4264	1895	887
1884	3972	1896	724

From Captain Hooper's report.

of rarity to the furriers. One would expect a furrier to know something about the animals upon which, after all, he depends for a living, but I have found out for myself that the average furrier does not even have the slightest knowledge of the most elementary zoology. One thought I was joking when I told him that the ermine is not white in summer; he also did not know that the opossum is a marsupial. Another one, believe it or not, did not know that a beaver is a rodent. But when they learned that the sea otter was rare and when this information was enforced by lack of supply, the prices shot up. And, of course, an especially fine specimen demanded a premium.

In 1910 there appeared in London a book by a Captain H. J. Snow, with the title *In Forbidden Seas*. The author had hunted sea otter for many years of his life, and although he tells a number of interesting facts one wonders much of the time whether they are facts. Captain Snow managed to misspell every name, personal as well as geographical, that was slightly more difficult than Smith or Brown, or less well known than London or New York. He informed his readers that a herd of sea otters was called a "pod" by the hunters because that is the Russian word for herd. Maybe the hunters called a sea-otter herd a "pod" but it could not have been for that reason; there is a Russian word *pod* but it means "under." Although I don't think much of Captain Snow's ability as a reporter, I do trust him when it comes to the pelts, and he wrote that "the finest skins are black, with white silvery hairs distributed evenly about 3/4 inch apart all over." He added that the value of the pelt depended on evenness of color but that the traders disregarded it if the head was of a different color. Snow said that the head "was often white" and claims to have seen one completely white pelt, presumably an albino.[4]

Such exceptionally fine pelts as those described by Snow

[4] Steller mentions that he saw white sea otter on Bering Island but thought that they were very old individuals.

did bring fantastic prices. In 1910 they brought over a thousand dollars—of course a woman's fur coat takes only two—and for later sales, prices of $3000 and $3500 for choice large specimens have been quoted. Whether these prices were actually paid is unproved, but in 1920 the official price was $2500. Then fashion changed for no discernible reason, and the pelts sold at auctions—they were certified as "legal" from the Kurile Islands—brought prices ranging from $125 to $410.

Although the sea otter has natural enemies, such as the killer whales, it succeeded in holding its own and increasing in numbers once its only effective enemy, Man, had legislated himself into the role of a bystander. In 1940 the sea otters of the Kuriles were estimated to number at least 700, with several hundred along the western Aleutians. Reports from elsewhere were still lacking then, and there later turned out to be a good reason for that. The areas not covered by reports then available were under the direct jurisdiction of the United States Fish and Wildlife Service. This agency was in the position of having to cover a coastline of several thousand miles with inadequate manpower. If unscrupulous people had tried to poach, the agency would not have been able to do much physically. The way to protect the sea otter was to adopt a military method and simply keep the breeding grounds secret. In 1950 the agency, after 40 years of sea-otter protection, felt that a little of this peculiar secrecy could be lifted, and it announced that there were more than 8000 sea otters along the Alaskan and Aleutian coasts.

The numbers of the California sea otter, for a while believed to have been zero, were around 200 in 1950.

To naturalists the sea otter is one of the most interesting animals alive, one of the interesting points being that its ancestry is unknown, and the one known fossil find only adds a complication. In structure the sea otter resembles the river otter *Lutra canadensis,* the shape of the teeth being the most pronounced major difference. As one naturalist described it: "If we liken the teeth of the river otter to freshly chipped rock, those of the sea otter can only be compared to worn pebbles." A fossil otter from the late Tertiary period, only a few million years in age, shows teeth intermediate between those of the sea otter and the Canadian otter. But this fossil has been found, of all places, in the so-called Siwalik beds in India!

Another interesting point is that the "old man of the sea," as the Fish and Wildlife Service called the sea otter, following old precedent, has changed habits during the period of persecution, and presumably because of it. Every writer from Steller to Ernest Thompson Seton asserted that sea otters were monogamous. They no longer are. Other habits have changed too. Captain Hooper was the first to note that they no longer came to the shore to rest or sleep. There are, of course, natural limits: the sea otter must live in places where the sea bottom is not out of its diving range, since its main food, the sea urchin, lives at the bottom and has to be taken by diving.

One would wish that the hunters after Steller had paid more attention to the sea otter's habits. It would be valuable to know whether the habits now established were also acquired in recent centuries. The sea otter is indubitably the most intelligent permanent inhabitant of the ocean, and it is the only mammal below the monkeys and apes which has progressed to the use of tools. The favorite position of the sea otter is floating on its back, and the sea urchins it acquires by diving are eaten off its own chest. When not eating, sea otters have been seen to play with a ball of kelp, tossing it from one forepaw to the other. They have also been seen to hold sea urchins, one in each paw, and knock them together to break the shells. But they have also been observed to place flat stones on their chests and smash the sea urchins by hitting them against the stones.

Nobody can tell whether this is a recent "invention," but another observed habit seems to be. When sea otters sleep

on the water—and this is one of the things they are supposed
not to have done in the past—they sleep on their backs. But
they do not want to drift out to the open sea where natural
enemies are around, so they moor themselves to seaweed.
They have been seen, fast asleep, clutching strands of living
and anchored seaweed between their forepaws, and also with
seaweed strands looped around their bodies. Female sea otters
—this is not necessarily a recent development—have been
observed to spank their children. The only other animal
known to do this is the Australian koala, one of the most
extreme tree dwellers now alive.

For lack of older observations we can't tell just how much
the sea otter has learned in a century. But we do know that
there was a change in habits, a "challenge and response," in
the course of which the old man of the sea has given us some
fascinating glimpses of what is possible. We might be able
to learn still more from him.

12: *The Old Ones*

THIS chapter begins in an area of our planet which is not mentioned again in the story, and at a time which is also not mentioned later on. The reason for this is that an ancient reptile which was named *Eunotosaurus africanus* lived in what is now the Cape Province of South Africa, a long distance from the places where the succeeding events occurred. Eunotosaurus lived in the Permian period, the name of which happens to be derived from the former administrative district of Perm in Imperial Russia, where formations from that period first became known. Chronologically the Permian period preceded the Triassic period, and since Eunotosaurus comes from the upper or late Permian it lived some 210 million years ago.

What is known of Eunotosaurus is not enough to provide a picture of its appearance when it was alive. We know a good portion of the skull bones—the teeth in its jaws were rather small—but we don't know how long its neck was. The tail is missing and of the limbs we have just one major bone of one leg. We do have enough of the pelvis to get a general idea and the same applies to the shoulders. And we do have the rib cage.

It is just this rib cage which makes Eunotosaurus important and, in the proper circles, even famous. There were ten ribs on either side of the spine but only the first and the tenth look reasonably like ribs, while numbers ii to ix have a weird shape. They are widened in the middle section to such an extent that they touch each other, while both ends are pointed. There is nothing directly comparable in the animal world; one would have to go to fairly technical concepts to find something that has about the same shape, as, for example, the "gores" of a plastic balloon, or the area enclosed by the 100th and 120th meridian. Or just say the outside of a section of an orange.

This Eunotosaurus was still rather close to the earliest of the reptiles, and it is believed to have been a burrowing form that needed the semi-armor provided by these wide ribs to withstand the pressure of the soil. The important point is that these ribs that are not yet fused but look as if they were on the verge of becoming so put Eunotosaurus in a class all its own. It has been called "the only known archichelonian." Linguistically, the last word is based on the Greek *archaios,* "very old" or "first in time," while *chelonē* is the Greek word for tortoise. Eunotosaurus was ancestral stock for the turtles and tortoises that were still to come.

All turtles and tortoises—zoologists, when they wish to refer to all of them, say "chelonians"—are built on a plan which would be less easy to understand if we did not have this example from the upper Permian of the Cape Province. The chelonians, as everybody knows, are enclosed in a solid box consisting of the "carapace" on top and the "plastron" underneath. This solid bony armor began with widening ribs that finally grew together and, extending both front and back, managed to overlap and enclose the shoulders and the pelvis, so that only head, limbs, and tail stick out, and in most cases these too can be drawn inside. There were no muscles covering the widening ribs on the outside, only skin which has changed into a horny covering. The process was completed very soon after the time of Eunotosaurus. A fossil true chelonian from the upper Triassic of Germany—logically named *Triassochelys*—shows its ancestry only in rudimentary teeth. All other chelonians, whether fossil or living, are as toothless as birds.

Although this early and, in more ways than one, tightly encased reptilian tribe originated on dry land—even, as far as we can tell, under desert conditions—it quickly discovered the other extreme, lakes and the open seas. To this day, nearly 200 million years later, we can see that its members tend to extremes of environment. On the one hand, we have the large and clumsy but merrily surviving desert tortoise of our southwestern deserts, while on the other hand we have the gracefully swimming green turtles and hawksbill turtles of the high seas, which touch land only for the serious business of depositing their eggs. Naturally the conquest of

EUNOTOSAURUS AFRICANUS

Pareiasaurus beds, South Africa (1914)

The incomplete skeleton of *Eunotosaurus,* the only known ancestral
form of the later turtles and tortoises

the open seas required some changes; the high-domed carapace of the land forms was lowered and smoothed out to reduce water resistance, in a number of fossil forms the solid armor was interrupted by "windows" to reduce weight, and the feet were changed into flippers.

And in all periods of geological history the chelonians have shown a remarkable tendency to produce forms of a size so colossal that it makes one understand the Hindu legends which say that the earth rests on the head of an elephant that, in turn, stands on the back of an enormous turtle. (It is considered bad manners to ask what supports the turtle.) When, during the upper Cretaceous period,

Kansas was flooded by the so-called Niobrara Sea, a gigantic turtle populated the warm waters, along with other marine reptiles. It was *Archelon ischyros* (this time the "arch" in the name is derived from Greek *archos,* meaning "first in rank" or "ruler") that measured more than 11 feet in length with a spread of the fore flippers of over 12 feet.

The marine turtles of today cannot quite compete with these titans of the past, but the leatherback turtle, *Dermochelys,* is still a colossal animal. One large specimen measured 9 feet in length and weighed 1500 pounds. The leatherback turtle, which is unfortunately growing rare, is interesting not only because of its record size but because it is a living high-seas form with greatly reduced armor. The original solid carapace and plastron which its ancestors must have had are reduced to ribs which are again free and to a large number of small bony plates imbedded in the tough skin.

The largest land tortoise known is also a fossil, but much younger geologically than Archelon. It lived during the late Tertiary period, not much more than a million years ago, and its habitat, by curious coincidence if you think of the Hindu legends, was India. It was found in the Siwalik beds of northern India—the same fossil-bearing strata which produced that doubtful ancestor of the sea otter—and was properly named *Colossochelys atlas* by the British naturalist Dr. Hugh Falconer in 1837, the *atlas* of course referring to that other mythological earth shoulderer. Hugh Falconer had only fragmentary remains at his disposal but he could compute that the carapace must have had a size of 12 feet, measured over the curve. A smaller but far more complete specimen, recovered in India by Dr. Barnum Brown, is on exhibit at the American Museum of Natural History in New York. Its carapace measures 7 feet, 4 inches, over the curve and is 5 feet wide; the tortoise must have weighed 2100 pounds when alive; and Dr. Brown believed that it was between 300 and 400 years old when it died.

A colossal land tortoise of great weight, aged 300 years, is not something that strikes a zoologist as being necessarily an item from the fossil record. Comparatively recent journals and books provide precisely the same picture.

When Captain John Jourdain made his voyage to the Seychelles in January 1609[1] the customary boat was sent ashore—to North Island—to look for water:

Butt because our men made noe signe of any water we ankored not. Soe the boate retourned and brought soe many land tortells as they could well carrie. Soe we stoode alonge towards the other islands. The tortelles were good meate, as good as fresh beefe, but after two or three meales our men would not eate them, because they did looke soe uglie before they were boyled; and so greate that eight of them did almost lade our skiffe.

Jourdain's shipmate Revett corroborated this; there were, he wrote, "land turtles of so huge a bidgnes which men will thinke incredible; of which our company had small lust to eate of, beinge such huge defourmed creatures and forted with five clawes lyke a beare."

From another ocean and about another set of islands, written almost precisely one century later than Jourdain's account, we have the report of the famous English buccaneer, the very literary pirate William Dampier:

The Spaniards when they first discover'd these Islands, found Multitudes of Guanoes, and Land-turtle or Tortoise, and named them the Gallapagos Islands. I do believe there is no place in the World that is so plentifully stored with those Animals. . . . The Land-turtle are here so numerous, that 5 or 600 Men might subsist on them alone for several Months, without any other sort of Provision: They are extraordinary large and fat; and so sweet, that no Pullet eats more pleasantly. One of the largest of these Creatures will weigh 150 or 200 weight, and some of them are 2 foot, or 2 foot 6 inches over the Challapee or Belly. I did never see any but at this place, that will weigh above 30 pound weight.[2]

[1] See Chapter 8.
[2] *A New Voyage Around the World*, by William Dampier. London, 1697.

This kind of news kept trickling in during the two centuries from 1600 to 1800. Traveler after traveler reported that they had landed on uninhabited islands where gigantic tortoises abounded. And most of them reported with relish that they were good to eat—the squeamishness of the men aboard John Jourdain's ship is an almost incredible exception—and thereby advertised to other sailors that fresh meat could be had on those islands.

Any modern reader of such old ships' journals sooner or later begins to wonder about the almost psychotic preoccupation with food on the part of the travelers, and it needs some mental effort to understand their reactions. Man went to sea before he was technologically ready to travel with certainty, not to mention with a reasonable amount of comfort. The wooden ships which discovered the globe lacked anything that would provide power at the will of the captain. They depended on the wind for propulsion, and at almost any moment the wind might increase to unmanageable strength or else might simply die away to a dead calm that might last for weeks if you were unlucky. The food situation was equally unreliable. Since the existence of bacteria was still unknown, the relatively simple process of canning food was still in the future. Refrigeration was an impossibility which nobody had ever even dreamed of, though on land the ice house was in use. Insect-killing poisons were unknown. So the food on board these ships consisted of heavily oversalted meat, sometimes beef, more often horse meat, dished out with the brine in which it floated. The other staple was hardtack, a bread so dry that no mold could get a root-hold (unless you were unlucky and the hardtack was swamped by water and could not be dried out fast enough), and limited quantities of dried beans and peas and lentils which were used up quickly before the weevils got into them. To make the bad situation worse, the ships were not undermanned, which would have meant more work per man, but also more food. On the contrary, they were as overmanned as possible, and not because some men might be lost in heavy weather. Every minute of day and night the owners had to think of enemies—somebody usually was at war with somebody else—and of pirates. Ships did carry guns, but the final act of any naval engagement was a hand-to-hand fight with a boarding party, and the more hands there were on board to wield a cutlass, knife, or spike, the better your chances. There was a certain safety in numbers.

The over-all result of these conditions was ships setting out on voyages of unknown durations, overmanned and understocked, so that everybody aboard, with the possible exception of the captain and the first mate, was forever and ever thinking and dreaming of something to eat, something "soft and sweet," something that was food, as contrasted to the subsistence offered by hardtack and salted meat. The interesting and often unique fauna of lonely islands suffered in consequence. And when some of the more foresighted captains, a good number of them buccaneers, put live goats and pigs ashore on islands for the sake of fresh meat at a later date, the island fauna suffered even more; instead of being subjected to the attacks of hungry (but transient) men, it was constantly exposed to the attacks of hungry pigs.

The men, if offered a choice, preferred meat that could be eaten not only while the ship was at anchor, but that could be taken aboard and kept fresh for some time. But to keep it fresh meant in those days that it had to be kept alive, and very little food was available aboard ship. It was the ability of the large tortoises to stay alive without any food that made them so desirable. But though the ships' crews would return with tales of the big tortoises, they did not bring any specimens. Sometimes an empty carapace was brought home as a curiosity, but even then, more likely than not, the bringer would be unsure or confused about the island on which the tortoise had been taken.

It is significant that two of the earliest books devoted specifically to turtles and tortoises, Walbaum's *Chelonographia* of 1782 and Johann Gottlieb Schneider's *Allgemeine Natur-geschichte der Schildkröten (General Natural History of the Turtles)* of 1783, do not mention the "large tortoises of distant isles" at all. It is of course possible that the authors of these books, living far from any seaport, simply had not heard about them. But it is equally likely that the news which they had received was so much in the rumor category that they decided not to make any mention of it until more was known.[3]

Things remained in a state of insufficient reporting for quite some time. That big tortoises were frequent on a certain group of islands in the Pacific Ocean was certain. That there were, or had been, large tortoises on a number of islands in the Indian Ocean was also known, but on which islands was already doubtful. And to try to classify the few carapaces that had been brought home seemed a hopeless task. Some were undated, the place of origin was not stated, or if it was stated one could be doubtful in many cases that the information was correct, and even if one knew that the label "Madagascar" was wrong one still could not say what the proper label should be. A few islands in the Indian Ocean came to be mentioned more and more frequently. They were Mauritius, Réunion, and Rodriguez, the atoll of Aldabra to the north of Madagascar, and a few tiny islands nearby. And the Seychelles. The Pacific island group was the Galápagos, but an occasional mention of Juan Fernández, "Robinson's Island," crept in.

Around 1860 a zoologist decided that where there was a puzzle there ought to be a solution and that finding the solution should be merely a matter of tenacious application. He was Albert C. L. G. Günther, M.D., Ph.D., "Keeper of the Department of Zoology" of the British Museum. After reading everything that might shed light on the problem of

---

[3] Schneider mentioned an older work by one Caldesi, printed in Florence in 1687, which I have not been able to obtain. But if Caldesi had said anything startling I suppose that Schneider would have quoted him.

giant tortoises, and carefully examining what specimens there were, Dr. Günther published a large work in which the existing knowledge was organized and systematized. The work was entitled *The Gigantic Land Tortoises (Living and Extinct) in the Collection of the British Museum* and was published by the museum in 1877. The proper cataloguing

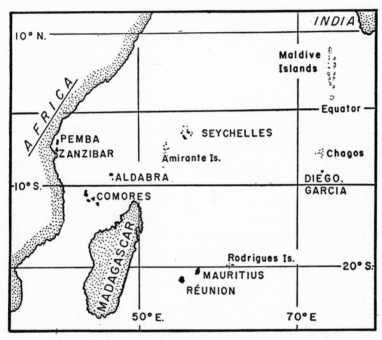

The various island groups north of Madagascar in the Indian Ocean, between the African coast and the mainland of India

of the specimens had been made possible because Dr. Günther had found an anatomical clue as to the origin of a preserved tortoise shell.[4] In short he could tell whether a label was right or wrong and what it should be.

[4] The clue involved the presence or absence of specific plates in the armor. "Günther's rule" read:
  (a) those with nuchal shield plate and with double gular plate: Aldabra
  (b) those without nuchal plate and with single gular plate: Mascarenes
  (c) those without nuchal plate but with double gular plate: Galápagos

Although Galápagos is much more famous for a long list of reasons, I prefer to start with the islands in the Indian Ocean, where giant tortoises were scattered over a much larger area. Three of the islands where they were found are known collectively as the Mascarenes, after their original discoverer, the Portuguese captain Pedro Mascarenhas. Strictly speaking, Mascarenhas discovered—in 1505—only two of the islands—Mauritius and Réunion. The third of the group, Rodriguez, was not discovered until 1545. Zoologically the Mascarenes, and especially Mauritius, are famous because they were the home of the dodo-like birds. But they were "tortoise islands," too. C. Grant, the author of the *History of Mauritius,* wrote in 1720: "We possess a great abundance of fowl, as well as both Land- and Sea-Turtle, which are not only a great resource for the supply of our ordinary wants, but serve to barter with the crews of ships who put in here for refreshment in their voyage to India." The sailors brought live dodos home with them, but with one probable exception, no specimen of the Mauritius tortoise was even taken to Europe. During the latter part of the seventeenth century a tortoise reached Paris which Pierre Perrault described as *La tortue des Indes* (the Indian Tortoise) because he had been told that it came from the Coromandel coast. The scientific name given was *Testudo indica* (*testudo* is the Latin word for tortoise) and later, after Perrault's death, *Testudo perraulti.* Since this type of tortoise does not exist on the Coromandel coast, or anywhere else in India, Dr. Günther concluded that the ship may have come from the Coromandel coast but picked up the tortoise on Mauritius on the return trip.

Though no fresh remains of the Mauritius tortoise were brought to Europe, old remains are known. They were found in a place locally called the *Mare aux Songes,* a part of the estate of Plaisance 3 miles from Mahébourg. There, intermixed with dodo bones, carapaces 2 to 3 feet in length were found, and Dr. Günther could establish three former

species, or subspecies, which he named *Testudo triserrata,*
T. inepta, and *T. leptocnemis.* We don't know whether
these same species, or one or two of them, also lived on
Réunion, because no remains of the Réunion tortoises are
known. But there are quite a number of eye-witness accounts
of tortoises on Réunion so that we can be sure of the fact
itself.

In P. J. Verhuff's *Voyage into the East Indies,* published
in Frankfort in 1633, there is a Latin entry about the arrival
at "Mascarene" (Réunion) on December 27, 1611. It says that
this is an island 80 miles from the island of Mauritius, 16
miles in circumference, uninhabited by people but with
many *Testudines* and fish.[5] The remarks of François Cauche
(1638) in his *Relation du Voyage à Madagascar* sound very
much the same. Writing in the French of his period he
reported:

*De la, nous tirasmes en l'isle de Mascarhene . . . scituée environ
deux degrez delà le Tropique du Capricorne. On y voit grand
nombre d'oiseaux, et tortues de terre, et les rivières y sont fort
pisqueuses.* (From there we proceeded to the isle of Mascarene . . .
situated about two degrees from the Tropic of Capricorn. One
can see large numbers of birds there, and land tortoises, and the
rivers are full of fish.)

Another report told that in 1712 a party of Frenchmen
coming from Madagascar landed on Réunion, and that they
lived for two years on fish, tortoises, and marine turtles—
presumably until they harvested their first crops. One more
witness is an abbé who wrote a letter (published in 1724 as
Lettre du Père Jacques) containing a virtual eulogy of the
Réunion tortoise:

*Le meilleur de tous les animaux, qu'on y trouve, soit par le
goût, soit pour la santé, c'est la Tortue de terre. . . . On assure*

[5] The original reads: *Die 27* [*mensis Decembris*] *pervererunt at Masqueri-
nem, iundam nempe, 80 miliaribus a Mauritii insula distantem, quae 16
miliaria circuitu et ambito suo continet, nec ullis hominibus habitatur, licet
ad victum necessarium Testudines piscesque et volucres multiplices abunde
suppeditet.*

qu'elle vit un temps prodigieux, qu'il lui faut plusieurs siècles pour parvenir à la grosseur naturelle, et qu'elle peut passer plus de six mois sans manger. (The best of all the animals one finds there, be it for the taste, be it for the health, is the land tortoise. . . . It is assured that it lives a prodigious time, that it needs several centuries to reach its full natural size, and that it can live for more than six months without eating.)

As for Rodriguez, we have the oft-quoted words of François Leguat, written in 1691, that "there are plenty of such land tortoises in this isle that sometimes you see two or three thousand of them in a flock, so that you may walk more than a hundred paces on their backs." Two specimens of this tortoise are in the Paris Museum—I don't know whether they reached Paris alive or not—and some additional bones and carapaces have been found on the island later after the tortoise was gone. The largest carapace measures 4½ feet over the curve and the bones prove that the tortoise was long-legged with a long neck. It obviously differed greatly from those of Mauritius, and Dr. Günther gave it the name *Testudo vosmoeri*.

The tortoises of the Mascarene Islands did not die out because sailors took numbers of them to keep on board as living meat; this would have diminished their numbers but would never have exterminated them. It was the settlement of the islands that spelled their doom. The men caught and cooked the large ones; their pigs and dogs ate the small ones and the eggs. And many small ones perished when the settlers burned off areas of brush to create fields for their crops.

The second group of Indian Ocean tortoises was those of Aldabra, an oval-shaped atoll to the north of Madagascar measuring more than 40 miles in circumference and enclosing a mostly shallow lagoon. Several deep channels split the atoll into four islands, of unequal length but generally of the same width of about 1½ miles. The island was known to, and named by, the Arabs, but the first recorded visit to it was by a Portuguese ship in 1511. Its fauna is typical for a lonely island in an ocean. The only mammals are two kinds of bats, of which one, *Pteropus aldabranus,* is not found anywhere else. Among the birds, one, a rail, is also typical for the island, while an ibis, *Ibis abottii,* is rare. The reptiles are represented by two geckos and one skink, and by *Chelone mydas* (the green turtle) and *Chelone imbricata* (the hawksbill turtle) at the shore. There are no amphibians, probably because they do not survive exposure to salt water. In short, all the rest of the fauna of Aldabra could easily have arrived

Testudo elephantina from Aldabra

As shown in Dr. Günther's *The Gigantic Land Tortoises*

from the neighboring land, and probably did, but how the Aldabra tortoise got there is a mystery.

Although the tortoise was common it was not mentioned until fairly late. The earliest literary reference to it seems to be an entry made on a map in 1744: "They found a great many land-turtle much larger than those at Rodrige."

When Dr. Günther pieced together the history of the by then already extinct Mascarene tortoises he felt that the Aldabra type could still be saved if measures to do so were taken at once. He wrote a long letter to the British Government, signed by the trustees and scientists of the British

Museum. The government responded quickly and promised all possible protection for the Aldabra tortoise. But, as has been said with reference to the coco-de-mer, protective measures, to be successful, must go further than just preserving what remnants there are. The remnants must be spread around to increase the area of the habitat, so that a local catastrophe cannot wipe out all the past efforts of the conservationists along with the protected species. In this case, this was done, and the place where the Aldabra tortoise did best was the home of the coco-de-mer, the Seychelles. Some spreading around had even been done before Dr. Günther wrote his plea.

When, in March 1899, the German oceanographic expedition on S.S. *Valdivia* under Professor Carl Chun visited the Seychelles for coco-de-mer, the members received proof of this distribution. "Mr. Harald Baty, the owner of Félicité," Professor Chun wrote,[6] "had sailed in the steam launch accompanied by my navigation's officer to his island and had taken one of the biggest and oldest of the giant tortoises (*Testudo elephantina*) from a small islet to present the expedition with the specimen. It was indeed an almost antediluvian looking monster which had been brought from Aldabra more than a hundred years ago—the grandfather of an aged Negro, a resident of Félicité, had already known this particular tortoise. Since Mr. Baty presented us with two other, though younger, specimens and Dr. Brooks added one as a present to His Majesty the Kaiser a fair number of dim-witted giants crawled around on board the *Valdivia*." Professor Chun added that most of the farms on the Seychelles keep a number of tortoises, of which one may be slaughtered for an especially festive occasion.

A later witness is Michael J. Nicoll, one of the two professional naturalists who have gone on record that they saw, in quiet water and in good weather, an unknown marine

---

[6] In his general account of the expedition, *Aus den Tiefen des Weltmeeres,* 2d ed. Jena, 1905, pp. 473-74.

animal which could only be called a "sea serpent."[7] His book, *Three Voyages of a Naturalist* (London, 1908), describes the trips he had made as the guest of the Earl of Crawford on the latter's yacht *Valhalla*. The *Valhalla* anchored at Aldabra but Mr. Nicoll did not see any of the tortoises there. He wrote that they were "once fairly abundant but are now confined to a small area on the northern side. The Hon. Walter Rothschild rents the island of Aldabra from the British Government and protects the tortoises as well as a peculiar species of ibis"—apparently Rothschild was always involved with ibises, even if they were disguised under names like Waldrapp. The reason Mr. Nicoll could not see the tortoises is that it would have been an exceedingly difficult overland trip, requiring more time than he had. He did get to see numbers of them in the Seychelles, "where they are kept in a semi-domesticated state." Mr. Nicoll reported that the usual means of confining them were low stone enclosures. Some were actually tethered, and all of them had identification numbers painted on their backs with white paint. Of course there were also some that lived in the bush without official owners.

In his work on the giant tortoises Dr. Günther distinguished several species of Aldabra tortoises. The most numerous one, and the one transplanted to the Seychelles, is *Testudo elephantina*. Another one he named *Testudo ponderosa,* and a third *Testudo daudinii*; however, it was said later that *T. daudinii* is probably identical with *T. elephantina* and that the one characteristic which made Dr. Günther think it a separate species was probably an individual characteristic of his specimen.

A specimen whose remains are preserved at the Royal College of Surgeons was named *Testudo hololissa* by Dr. Günther. While there is no doubt that it is a different species one may have doubts about Günther's insistence that it was from Aldabra.

[7] See *The Lungfish, the Dodo, and the Unicorn*, Chapter 7.

The catalogue of the College contains a rather detailed
history of the specimen. It was originally captured by Frenchmen. It was, the catalogue said, "a native of the Seychelle
Islands, and was being sent to General de Caën, Governor
of the Isle of France, in the French corvette *Gobemouche*
which was captured by Captain Corbett of H.M.S. *Nereida,*
and the animal was brought to the Cape of Good Hope. It was
sent to England by Admiral Bertie, who commanded at the
Cape, and remained in a living state at Petworth, the seat of
the Earl of Egremont, from August 1809 until April 1810.
Its weight was 207 pounds." Dr. Günther brushed the first
sentence aside by saying, "We have no evidence of tortoises
on the Seychelles," and declared that *Testudo hololissa* therefore must be a fourth species from Aldabra. Apparently
Dr. Günther was not acquainted with Jourdain's journal,
which is as clear on this point as is possible. If the French
said that they captured the tortoise on the Seychelles they
probably did. But what happened to the large numbers seen
by Jourdain's men we simply don't know.

There are other minor mysteries, and one major one, left.
In 1893 a French naturalist named Sauzier came to Port
Louis on Mauritius. Learning that an old tortoise was kept
on the drill ground of the artillery barracks, he went and
measured it. The carapace, not measured over the curve but
straight, was 40 inches long. The tortoise looked about 200
years old to him and upon inquiry he was told that it had
been there since 1810 and that it had grown very little, if
any, since then. Trying to establish the species, Sauzier
looked for the nuchal shield plate and found it lacking, as
Dr. Günther had specified for Mascarene tortoises, but instead of having a single gular plate underneath, it had a
double one and that combination, according to Dr. Günther's
scheme, made a Galápagos tortoise of it. Now it was con-
ceivable, though neither proved nor likely, that a ship with
a living Galápagos tortoise aboard had restocked its supplies
on Mauritius and that the tortoise, presumably still fairly

small then, had escaped and established itself in its new home until captured once more. Sauzier found it easier to believe that it was a survivor from the early days and named it *Testudo soumeirei*. Then he dug from the Mare aux Songes four damaged plastrons of tortoises, all with double gular plates which made them either Aldabra or Galápagos. Living Aldabra tortoises on Mauritius would be easy to account for, but subfossil Aldabra tortoises are less easy.

The main problem, of course, is how the giant tortoises got to the various islands at all. They existed on the Mascarenes, the Seychelles, and Aldabra. Madagascar, though it did not preserve a living form, did have giant tortoises until, say, a thousand years ago. As told in Chapter 8, scientists of the nineteenth century assumed that all these islands, including the Comoro Islands, which have a fauna resembling that of Madagascar, were leftover pieces of a former continent that was called Lemuria because of the lemurs of Madagascar, the Comoros, and India. With equal if not greater justification this hypothetical continent could have been called Testudina, but if it had been invented for the sake of the big island tortoises it would not have reached all the way to India. The continent of Lemuria became unnecessary when fossil lemurs turned up in Africa—the lemurs of Madagascar could then be explained by assuming a former connection between Africa and Madagascar only. But even if one postulated "Testudina," Aldabra would still have to be explained separately because it is now certain that Aldabra is an atoll which never had any land connection; this shows clearly in its fauna too. But if Aldabra has to have a separate explanation, why not separate explanations for Mauritius, Réunion, Rodriguez, and so forth?

There must be an answer, but it hasn't been found so far.

We now come to the "Western tortoise islands," the Galápagos, situated precisely under the equator some 600 miles to the west of the west coast of South America. They are a handful of fairly large islands, and another handful of smaller islands, plus a collection of islets, rocks, and cliffs, all of them volcanic. Though heated during the day by the equatorial sun they cool rapidly after sunset, and in general do not have the climate one would expect of islands under the equator, because they are located in the cold Humboldt current. The Humboldt current produces rather confused local currents between the islands, and just as a sailor without previous experience could not predict what the current is going to be like in a given spot he also could not predict what kind of beach he would find on the island he sees on the horizon. Most likely the beach consists of lava, piled high and dangerous to climb because it is loose, but it could be dense mangrove, and it could even be sandy. But whatever the beach is like the area near the shore will be arid in virtually every case, with a vegetation of prickly cactus and even more prickly bushes of other kinds. The more fertile places occur farther inland, or, rather, higher up, which on volcanic islands is more or less the same thing.

This amazing collection of islands was discovered by accident in 1535, mostly because Francisco Pizarro misbehaved after the conquest of Peru. To create some kind of order the bishop of Panama, Tomás de Berlanga, was requested to sail to Peru. He did sail on February 23, 1535, but the voyage did not go well. The captain, Diego de Rivadeneira, "navigated" by hugging the shore line—actually avoiding navigation by doing so—and as the ship approached the equator the wind suddenly died. After floating for a number of days the ship began to drift; it had been caught in the still unknown Humboldt current. The coastline vanished in the east and for weeks nothing was visible but water. On March 10 islands came into sight. The ship landed in the usual quest for water, but there wasn't any. There were birds of all kinds by the thousands, there were sun-heated lava rocks, there were coldly staring reptilian eyes, and there were spiny plants—from their appearance any botanist could have deduced lack

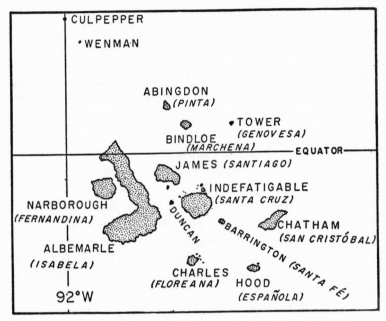

The Galápagos Islands, with customary English and official
Spanish names

of water at a glance. The men sent ashore to find water for
the ship's company and grass for the horses carried aboard
found neither the one nor the other. As the bishop later
wrote to the king of Spain: "They found nothing but seals
and turtles and such big tortoises that each could carry a man
on top of itself, and many iguanas that are like serpents."

After saying Mass several days later on another island—for
it was Passion Sunday—the bishop's men finally did find some
water and they then somehow made their way back to South
America, having lost two men and ten horses because of
thirst. The bishop, in his report to the king, stressed the
aridity of the islands and wrote that he did not think that
there was a place on them where one might sow a bushel of
grain. In short, he reported the discovery but said the islands
were worthless, which impression must have been strong

because they had not bothered to take possession of the islands for the king. The bishop did not even name them. And the first name they received is not the name that was later used. About 15 years after their discovery, Captain Diego de Rivadeneira, who had become hopelessly involved in the fights of the various Spanish factions, began to look around for a place where he would be safely out of the way of current events and remembered the bishop's islands. He reached them, but the unknown and fairly strong currents running between the islands did not let him land. Capitán de Rivadeneira decided after a while that it was not his ship which drifted around unpredictably but that he was among shifting islands. They were obviously enchanted. That the bishop had been able to land was only further proof; the enchantment could not stand up against the bishop's cross. So Diego de Rivadeneira called them *Los Encantadas,* the Enchanted Isles.

This name did not take hold, but their permanent name was given them by a European, the mapmaker Abraham Ortelius (né Oertel) who received a report on Berlanga's report. The outstanding thing about the islands was not the aridity—that could be found elsewhere too—but the large tortoises. In Spanish a tortoise is *galápago* and on Ortelius's map of 1587, *Typus Orbis Terrarum,* they appear as *Yslas de los galopegos.* Although Bishop Tomás de Berlanga had clearly said in his letter to the king of Spain that the islands were between 1/2 degree and 1 1/2 degrees below the equator— correct for most of them—Ortelius placed them quite a distance north of the "line." They appear to the west of Panama and are far too close to the mainland, but there can be no doubt that the real Galápagos are meant—they had just drifted a little, as Rivadeneira had expected all along.

The captains who sailed the Pacific probably had better charts than the Ortelius map; otherwise it might explain why the islands were left alone for a century. The real reason

is different, of course, and there is more than one. To begin
with, the Spaniards were fully occupied in South America;
they were still hunting semi-mythical or fully mythical gold
treasures and were fighting against Nature, against the Indians, and among themselves. Another reason for the neglect
is that the Galápagos are the Galápagos—large heaps of lava
almost impossible to walk on, with an unreliable water
supply which is meager when not nonexistent, with occasional volcanic eruptions. Moreover, unlike the Mascarenes,
stepping stones on the voyage to India, the Galápagos were
not even near a trade route; one did not visit them *en passant*.

After this century of neglect, the period of the buccaneers
began, also lasting about a century. William Dampier's book
of 1697 has already been quoted; his fellow buccaneer
Ambrose Cowley had visited the islands in 1684. Cowley
produced the first chart of them, and a fairly accurate one.
But though buccaneers went there whenever they felt like
it—islands *off* a trade route were just what they needed on
occasion—and occasionally met, the quality of the buccaneers
declined visibly and rapidly. The days of the gentleman
pirate who would report on what had been found and seen
and thereby enrich geographical knowledge were gone. The
second-string pirates who came afterward probably considered themselves clever if they could follow the indications
of the mariner's compass and read a chart. But they did know
from Cowley's book that the islands "were very plentifully
stored with the aforesaid Provisions, as Tortoises, Fowls, Fish
and Alguanoes, large and good."

After the century of the buccaneers and the privateers had
passed, the period of the whalers began; it did not last quite
a century. In 1593 Sir Richard Hawkins had deliberately
avoided the Galápagos, not even paying them a curiosity
visit;[8] in 1793 Captain James Colnett of the Royal Navy was

---

[8] The sentence: "Some fourscore leagues to the westward of this cape lyeth
a heape of Illands the Spaniards call Ilhas de los Galápagos; they are desert
and bear no fruite," is the sum total of what Hawkins had to say about them.

officially sent there. Not only to the Galápagos, of course, but
he was instructed to visit them, for Captain Colnett's trip had
the purpose of finding out where British whalers might make
port in the Pacific for repairs, refitting, and "victualling."
The Galápagos were one of the places he recommended (with
some reservations), but the whalers had already found the
islands for themselves. They had even established a post
office, at Post Office Bay on Charles Island. It consisted of
a barrel. There was no clerk, no postage, and no formalities.
Outward-bound ships left letters for home, or for other ships,
in the barrel, and the next homeward-bound ship took them
along. By about 1810, although the majority of the whalers
were still from Dover, England, there were some from
Nantucket and New Bedford.

In 1812 the U.S. frigate *Essex,* fully provisioned for a long
cruise and commanded by Captain David Porter (with a
midshipman named David Farragut aboard), entered the
Pacific with sealed orders. When the orders were opened
they said simply that Captain Porter was to drive the British
whalers from the Pacific as soon as war was declared. When
war was declared, American whalers guided Captain Porter
to the Galápagos and to Post Office Bay. The letters in the
barrel told better than any intelligence report what English
vessels were in the Pacific and where they might be at the
moment. Within a week Porter captured eleven ships. When
the war was over, most of the whaling ships in the Pacific
were from Nantucket and New Bedford. They sailed south
along the continental coast, rounded the always difficult
Cape Horn, and proceeded northward on the other side of
the continent in the Humboldt current, thus making the
Galápagos, to the detriment of the giant tortoises.

While the ships rode at anchor, crewmen went "turpining," as the logbooks expressed it. Apparently none of these
New England captains, or their first mates, had ever heard
the word tortoise, or if they had they did not use it. They

sent their men ashore for turpin, tarpain, terapen, turupin, tarphin, or terrepin. They all ate tortoise steak or tortoise stew afterward and assured one another that fried tortoise liver was the best thing a man could possibly eat. And they took a good supply of tortoises along with them, alive, when they hoisted anchor. The logbook entry of the *Sukey* of Nantucket, made June 14, 1812, is typical: "I leave this port [Charles Island] this Day with 250 Turpin."

Giant tortoises from the Galápagos Islands

At the time the whalers were pursuing their trade, hardly any of them wrote anything longer than a logbook entry, but a few captains wrote reminiscing memoirs after their retirement. The following is an account of "turpining" as it took place in 1858 on Albemarle Island:[9]

After everything was put in shape [aboard ship] about two thirds of the crew went ashore, taking with us boat sails to make

[9] From *Strange but True* by Captain Thomas Crapo, published in New Bedford in 1893. Captain Crapo's ship was the bark *Greyhound*.

tents of and water to drink and cook with, as fresh water cannot
be found there. After fitting up our temporary camp we started
for the mountains after turpin, which are very numerous, and
are not found on any other islands.

Turpin are a specimen of turtle, the shell being in large checks
like an alligator's skin, and their flesh is unsurpassed as food for
soups and stews: its equal cannot be found. The liver is far
superior to any kind of meat I ever ate. It is as large as a beef
critter's (from a large one) and is many times superior to it in
any way you choose to cook it.

In order to get them we had to go high up in the mountains,
as that seems to be their roaming ground. They are black in color
and move very slow. We did not disturb the large ones, as we
would have had to kill and cut them up and carry the pieces
down on our backs, as many of them will weigh, I should think,
nearly half of a ton. So we caught the smaller ones, none weighing
over five or six hundred.

We went hunting them every day for a week, and as they are
so clumsy and move so slow, made it an easy matter to capture
them. We built a pen to put them in, and while on shore lived on
them mostly and used hard bread from the ship for soups and
stews and other ways: the cook dished it out to us. The small
ones we caught we carried down to camp on our shoulders, but
we had to drag the large ones. They are perfectly harmless and
never known to bite. We caught about a hundred during the time.
At the close of the week we took them aboard. Their weights
would range from about five pounds to five hundred and over.
We put them on deck and between decks, and let them crawl
around as they chose. It was all of six months before they were
all gone. I never knew one to eat or drink a drop while they
were on board, and yet they looked as fat as a ball of butter when
they were killed.

In order to estimate the number of tortoises that had lived
on the Galápagos at the time the whalers made it a regular
port of call, Dr. Charles Haskins Townsend of the New York
Aquarium examined a total of 79 preserved logbooks of
whaling vessels in the libraries of New Bedford, Nantucket,

and Salem.[10] The logbooks covered the period 1831–1868, during which time the 79 vessels made 189 visits to the islands. Their combined catch numbered 13,013 tortoises. Since the American whaling fleet at that time numbered around 700 vessels, the 79 logbooks represent only a little more than 10 per cent of the whole. Naturally not all 700 vessels went to the Pacific Ocean; on the other hand, whaling vessels of other nationalities did; the number of tortoises actually taken during these four decades might well be 50,000. The inroads made by the buccaneers before the whalers came can be more or less neglected, even though the figures, if they were available, might look fairly large. Unlike those of the whalers, the visits of the buccaneers were not a steady commercial operation.

The islands from which the whalers took tortoises are Albemarle, Chatham, Charles, Hood, James, Abingdon, Duncan, Indefatigable, and Barrington. The island of Jervis is mentioned only once, and the fairly large island of Narborough is not mentioned at all, the reason probably being that there was a major volcanic eruption on Narborough early in the nineteenth century. The buccaneers may have taken tortoises from Narborough in their time; in more recent times only a single specimen, an old male, has been recorded there.

The wonder is, of course, that the tortoises lasted as long as they did. That they were numerous before the whalers systematically provisioned themselves with tortoise is easily explained. A tortoise of this type will produce around twenty eggs per year. If there are no natural enemies that eat the eggs the activity of a single couple of adults will result in two hundred young tortoises after only ten years and soon the first batch of the young ones will start laying more eggs.

[10] See "The Galápagos Tortoises in Their Relation to the Whaling Industry" by Charles H. Townsend, in *Zoologica, Scientific Contributions of the New York Zoological Society*, vol. IV, no. 3, July 29, 1925.

Because of the longevity of the individual tortoise, the off-spring of each female will be numerous, and for the same reason the number of individuals will be enormous, since a score of generations can be alive at the same time. Given a sufficient supply of plant food and the absence of enemies, you get an island virtually paved with tortoises, just as Leguat described it.

The reason the tortoises lived so much longer on the Galápagos than on the Mascarenes is mostly the size and the topography of the islands. Albemarle is 72 miles long and 10 miles wide in the north, 20 miles wide in the south, with elevations up to 5000 feet. Indefatigable is 20 miles across with its highest point 2296 feet above sea level. Chatham measures 24 by 8 miles with a 2500-foot peak, and Narborough is 15 miles across, with a 4300-foot volcano. There were always places on these islands where people could not penetrate. And as long as the supply was really large, the sailors practiced an unconscious conservation program for their own convenience. Small tortoises were spurned because they did not have enough meat, which means that they were left to grow up. And the sailors did not take the very biggest specimens because they were too heavy to move. Captain Crapo's report is already atypical in regard to the size of the tortoises taken. In the days preceding him the rule was to look for specimens weighing between 50 and 75 pounds, which a man could easily carry on his back.

In the middle of whaling activity and "turpining," something else happened: on September 15, 1835, H.M.S. *Beagle* arrived at Chatham Island. The purpose of the voyage was an oceanographic survey around South America. Nobody even asks any more whether H.M.S. *Beagle* accomplished her mission or not, the offshoot of the expedition was so much more important than the expedition itself. For the young man on board H.M.S. *Beagle,* who served as the "naturalist" of the expedition, was named Charles Darwin, and the theory of evolution was born while he was on the

Galápagos. But that came later. Darwin, after his return to England, first published his ponderous but very well-written *Journal of Researches* (1839). Now the eyes of science were on the Galápagos and they have stayed on these islands ever since.

Enough had been learned about the past of our planet by the middle of the nineteenth century to cast a special and strange and most intriguing light on these islands. There was this piece of land, somewhat broken up, right under the equator. It teemed with unwieldy tortoises. At the black lava shores there lived something that did not exist any-where else in the world any more—a sea-going lizard. These large black iguanas, by the tens of thousands, sat motionless in the surf and swam out into the sea to feed on seaweed. Farther up there were thousands of other large iguanas, also vegetarian in their habits, colored sulfur-yellow and red. There were many other smaller lizards and a snake. It looked as if these islands had been bodily left over from the time when the reptiles were the dominant form of life on earth. And just as there had been a few small mammals of insignificant size in the time of the dinosaurs, there was a little mammalian life on the islands: a few bats, which might have been brought there by a storm, and various species of a white-footed rodent, a specimen of which Darwin had caught and which later had been described as *Mus galapagoensis,* the "mouse from the Galápagos." The "white-footed mouse" became a symbol, the only mammal among the dragons on the islands time forgot.

I am sorry to have to say that the Galápagos are not a "Lost World" and that the true explanation is somewhat different, but this romantic, though mistaken, picture provided a powerful stimulus for continued interest.

First the zoological picture was rounded out. There were about sixty kinds of land birds. About two dozen different reptiles. No amphibians. No mammals except for the bats and the "mouse" (really a small rat) in several species. Several hundred insects. The sea life was plentiful: fishes and marine reptiles (turtles), seals, and marine birds. Two of the latter were especially interesting: a smallish penguin which, living under the equator, is the most northerly penguin in existence, and a flightless cormorant.

The big tortoises remained the center of attraction even for the zoologist, who felt that he had still come in time here while the opportunity had been missed on the Mascarenes. Dr. Albert Günther in his work on the gigantic land tortoises provided a separate section for the "Races of the Galápagos Tortoises." He listed six of them, as follows:

Testudo elephantopus	(James Island?)
Testudo nigrita	(?)
Testudo vicina	(Albemarle, South)
Testudo microphyes	(Albemarle, North)
Testudo ephippium	(Charles Island)
Testudo abingdoni	(Abingdon Island)

Nobody could be quite sure at the time Dr. Günther wrote his book which species were rare or how the fate of the giant tortoises as a whole was progressing. Unfortunately it progressed badly. If the islands had been left alone after the whalers stopped going there, the tortoises would probably have recovered; enough specimens were left, either in inaccessible places, or too big or too small for the whalers' purpose, to perpetuate themselves. But Ecuadorians settled on the islands and killed off tortoises for their oil. Even worse, domesticated animals had been released—or had escaped from ships—from time to time. The goats did no harm, but the pigs and the dogs decimated the young tortoises especially.

Zoologists decided that a serious effort ought to be made at least to learn what could still be learned, even if it might be too late for salvage. In 1905 the California Academy of Sciences organized a major expedition to Galápagos and collected 266 specimens. These became the subject of a special study by Dr. John Van Denburgh, who distinguished not less than fifteen species. Sorted by islands, his list looks like this:

Albemarle	$\left\{\begin{array}{l} \textit{T. guntheri, T. vicina, T. microphyes,} \\ \textit{T. becki,} \text{ and one unnamed} \end{array}\right.$
Narborough	*T. phantastica*
Charles	*T. elephantopus;* extinct
Hood	*T. hoodensis*
Chatham	*T. chathamensis*
Indefatigable	*T. porteri*
Duncan	*T. ephippium*
Jervis	*T. wallacei*
James	*T. darwini*
Abingdon	*T. abingdoni*
Barrington	*T.* sp. (unnamed); extinct

Only on Duncan, Indefatigable, and Albemarle were the tortoises still "numerous" or "fairly abundant"; for everywhere else the label read "rare," "very rare," or "nearly extinct."

The prediction that the next decade would see the extinction of several more species was the obvious conclusion to be drawn from this list. But in 1917 Professor Samuel Garman of Harvard University went over the anatomy of the Galápagos tortoises once more and came to the conclusion that Dr. Van Denburgh had been somewhat too enthusiastic a systematizer. Professor Garman emphasized that young Galápagos tortoises cannot be distinguished as to species or island of origin. The older they grow the more clearly the various characteristics appear. And the characteristics keep changing with age. What had happened was that too much attention had been paid to anatomy and too little to the living animal. In other words, specimens of different age had been classified as different species. That, of course, should not happen, but it does; it has even happened that the two sexes of a species were classified separately, though not necessarily in the case of the Galápagos tortoises.

The species *Testudo phantastica,* based on the single specimen from Narborough Island, was simply a very old *Testudo elephantopus,* probably changed a little more by recovery from volcanic burns. Van Denburgh's "nearly extinct"

Testudo abingdoni was also just a very old *T. elephantopus.*
Garman threw out a whole raft of other names as mere
"synonyms": *T. becki, T. hoodensis,* and *T. ephippium* were
all young or middle-aged specimens of *T. elephantopus.* Like-
wise *T. galapagoensis* and *T. wallacei* were "synonyms" of
Testudo nigra. More important even than the removal of a
lot of superfluous names was the fact that Professor Garman
could show that the Galápagos tortoise did not stand as isolated in the system as had been believed and taught for two
generations. A tortoise known for a long time—it appeared in
literature for the first time in Walbaum's *Chelonographia*
way back—was proved to be a relative of the Galápagos
tortoise. It occurs in the northern portions of South America
but is mainly found in Central America, grows to a length of
two feet, and is easily and often tamed. Locally it is called
"jaboty"; the scientific name is *Testudo tabulata.*

The realization that there was a living relative of the
Galápagos tortoise on the mainland changed a lot of thoughts.
Up to the time that Garman's work was published, all that
naturalists could offer by way of helpful information was that
a fossil tortoise resembling the Galápagos tortoise had been
found on Cuba. This piece of knowledge had merely deepened
the mystery, but with *Testudo tabulata* identified as a related
mainland form, it helped to clarify the situation. In some
manner the ancestor of the jaboty—possibly indistinguish-
able from the living form—had reached the Galápagos and
changed to the Galápagos tortoise. If this ancestral tortoise
had spread westward to Galápagos there was no reason why
it could not have spread eastward to Cuba, where it presumably did not survive because of people and other mammals.

The case of the jaboty was new ammunition for a long-
smoldering debate. The debate had been started in all inno-
cence by Charles Darwin, who, looking at the islands and
finding no land that was not volcanic, concluded that the
islands had been built up by a probably long succession of
volcanic eruptions from the bottom of the sea. They were

islands which had been isolated since the time they originated, never connected to the mainland. Late in the nineteenth century Dr. George Baur declared that Darwin had
been wrong in this case. The Galápagos, Dr. Baur was convinced, were "islands of subsidence," which means islands
formed by the process of the settling of a land mass so that in
the end only the highest peaks still appear above water.
Because the fauna seemed to be a little more closely related
to Central American than to South American types, a former
land bridge from Panama to the Galápagos was assumed,
taking in Cocos Island as another point that had been high
enough to have survived as an island.

John Van Denburgh applauded this idea enthusiastically,
mostly on the grounds that the tortoises cannot swim. He
admitted that they float, but they will drift helplessly with
the ocean currents. And if they drifted ashore somewhere
they would be so battered as to die soon after. This was the
reason that each island where tortoises occurred had its own
species of tortoise, and only one species, except for large
Albemarle Island which had several. "If the transportation
of tortoises from one island to another does not occur," he
concluded his argument, "there is little reason to believe that
tortoises, at some time in the past, have drifted over the vastly
greater distance from some continent, and have reached each
of the eleven islands on which they have been found. Nor do
we know whence they have come. . . ."

William Beebe, who apparently never read Garman's
work, accepted all this at face value but had to contradict
one point: during his visit to Galápagos he had seen a tortoise
swim and swim well. The tortoise had died a week later and
was found to have congested lungs as well as a congested
small intestine, and Beebe inclined to the belief that the
tortoise, though it could swim, died of the salt water it had
swallowed on that occasion. Whether this conclusion is correct or not is relatively unimportant; much of Van Denburgh's argument is based on his own overclassification.

At the present practically everybody is agreed that there is precious little, if any, geological evidence for a former land bridge to Panama. And the viewpoint of the zoologists (with which the botanists agree) has been beautifully expressed by one of them, who asked: "If there was a land bridge, why was it so little used?" Remember: a few mice, some bats, five dozen land birds, two dozen reptiles, no amphibians. The whole fauna is such that it could have arrived by ocean current: the penguins swimming; the finches, the rodents, and the reptiles on drifting trees—all, that is, except the tortoises.

Samuel Garman suspected that they might have been transported by people, prehistoric South Americans. We now know much better than was known in 1917 how far a balsa raft can drift from South America. Such a raft could certainly drift to the Galápagos and the prehistoric South Americans might also have carried tortoises as living food. Since nobody knows how long it took the Galápagos tortoises to differentiate from *Testudo tabulata* or a similar tortoise, there is no way of calculating backward in order to find out whether the prehistoric South Americans built rafts at a sufficiently early date. Nor do we know just when they built rafts first. The thought, therefore, must remain an interesting idea, unproved and unprovable.

In spite of everything, the giant tortoise is still with us. In 1928 an expedition to the Galápagos led by Dr. Townsend collected 180 of them, which were placed in colonies in California, Arizona, Texas, Florida, and Bermuda, to save them from extinction and let them survive, even in the same kind of semidomesticated state as the Aldabra tortoises on Mahé. It is even possible that there are some small natural colonies on unimportant and therefore neglected islands in the Pacific, descendants of tortoises which were taken for food by buccaneers and later by whalers but which escaped. At one time Galápagos tortoises were established on Juan Fernández, but these were eaten later. It would be interesting to check over the Marquesas, because in 1813 Captain Porter, when on Madison Island, the principal island of the group, gave some tortoises to the chiefs as presents and let a large number escape into the bushes. Similarly, Captain James Cook gave a Galápagos tortoise, part of his ship's food supply, to the king of Tongatabu of the Tonga Islands in 1777. A compound was built for it and it is still a pet of the royal household.

The islands themselves present a far more difficult problem, largely because it is an international problem. Their unique and irreplaceable life forms are succumbing to wild pigs and wild dogs. At least a number of the islands should be put under strictest protection, all the not-indigenous fauna removed, and the islands left alone. Even though they are not, as was once believed, remains of the past which are still in the age of the reptiles, they should be restored to the enchantment of their uniqueness.

Head of a Galápagos tortoise

Sequence and Duration
of Geological Periods

Index

Sequence and Duration of Geological Periods

The total age of the earth must be more than 3500 million years and is probably nearer 4000 million. Geological history is divided into six "eras," and further subdivided into "periods" and "subperiods." The names of the eras and of some of the other divisions are based on Greek root words, which are given in the following table; for other names, the language of origin or geographical source is given. The notes under "Events" chiefly refer to facts mentioned in the text.

ERAS	PERIODS	SUBPERIODS	EVENTS
AZOIC (*azoos* = lifeless) Began 4000 million years ago; duration about 2000 million years	None	None	Gradual accumulation of the planetary mass; later formation of present atmosphere and oceans
ARCHAEOZOIC (*archaios* = first in time + *zoon* = animal) Began 1850 million years ago; duration 650 million years	Lower Pre-Cambrian (Cambria, Latin name for Wales)	Not recognizable	Origin of life; single-celled life in water
PROTEROZOIC (*proteros* = before) Began 1200 million years ago; duration 650 million years	Upper Pre-Cambrian	Not recognizable	Primitive marine life

PALEOZOIC (*palaios* = old) Began 550 million years ago; duration 355 million years		
	Cambrian Duration 70 million years	Primitive invertebrate sea life, slowly increasing in number of species through both periods
	Ordovician (Latin: *Ordovices*, people of early Britain) Duration 85 million years	
	Silurian (Latin: *Silures*, people of early Wales) Duration 40 million years	First fishes
	Devonian (From Devonshire, England) Duration 50 million years	More fishes. One of these early types still exists near the Comore Islands
	Carboniferous (Latin: *carbo* = coal + *fero* = to bear) Duration 85 million years	Period of maximum coal formation; early insects and amphibians
	Permian (From district of Perm, Russia) Duration 25 million years	Early reptiles; early mammals; *Eunotosaurus*

For all these periods, specialists distinguish subperiods based on local formations, usually labeled with place names

(*Continued on next page*)

ERAS	PERIODS	SUBPERIODS	EVENTS
MESOZOIC (*mesos* = middle) Popular name "Age of Reptiles" Began 195 million years ago; duration 135 million years	Triassic (*trias* = triad) Duration 35 million years	Lower Triassic, or Bundsandstein (German: *Bund* = colorful + *Sandstein* = sandstone)	Early saurians
		Middle Triassic, or Muschelkalk (German: *Muschel* = clam + *Kalk* = limestone)	Earliest known flying fish
		Upper Triassic, or Keuper (Old miners' term)	*Triassochelys*; pseudosuchians
	Jurassic (From Jura Mountains) Duration 35 million years	Black Jurassic, or Lias (French: *liais* = smooth, hard stone)	Marine reptiles: dinosaurs
		Brown Jurassic, or Dogger (Provincial English = round stone)	
		White Jurassic, or Malm (Middle English = sand)	Flying reptiles; *Archaeornis*
	Cretaceous (Latin: *creta* = chalk) Duration 65 million years	Lower Cretaceous (Smaller subdivisions usually bear Latinized place names for special formations)	Maximum development of dinosaurs; earliest known flightless (fishing) birds; marsupials like opossum; *Archelon*
		Upper Cretaceous (Smaller subdivisions as in Lower Cretaceous)	

CENOZOIC (*kainos* = new) Popular name "Age of Mammals" Began 60 million years ago		
Tertiary (Latin: *tertius* = the third. Named when there were thought to have been only three geological periods or eras) Duration slightly less than 60 million years	Paleocene (*palaios* + *kainos*)	First nonmarsupial mammals, or placentals
	Eocene (*eos* = dawn)	Amber; rich insect fauna
	Oligocene (*oligos* = a little)	
	Miocene (*meios* = less)	Steady increase of mammals
	Pliocene (*pleios* = more)	"Eoliths"; *Colossochelys*; only known fossil sea(?) otter
Pleistocene (*pleistos* = most + *kainos*) Popular name "Ice Age"; formerly called Diluvial period, from Latin *diluvium*, flood Duration about 1 million years; ended 10,000 to 15,000 years ago		Several glaciations; mammalian fauna quite like the present; various forms of early man; probable time of formation of Galápagos Islands
Holocene (*holos* = entire + *kainos*) Formerly called Alluvial period, from Latin *alluvio*, river deposits The geological present		Animals and plants of the geological present; known as "recent"

Index

Figures in italics refer to illustrations; those followed by *n* refer to footnotes.